THE
STREET
ANALYST

JEAN P

Published by
Panacea Development Group LLC
MIAMI, FL
Thestreetanalysts.com

ISBN: 978-1-7358672-0-5

Edited by Brandy C. Lucas
Interior & Cover by Gary A. Rosenberg

CONTENTS

This is for you; for all the young black men and women who embraced difficulties and made their problems the learning curve for success!

ACKNOWLEDGMENTS

It's so hard to name just a few people when you realize that the whole world conspired to give you a helping hand, unconsciously. This has been a battle from the beginning to the end, but we never gave up.

To my partners Scooboo (Tallahassee, FL) and the Billionaire Book Club, thank you. Fred A.K.A Dre from Detroit, MI, through your wisdom and knowledge, you helped me shape my vision, which allowed me to create. Truthfully, without your constant reminder that I had a book to get back to, I would have never gotten this done. To all those who knew not to fuck with me while I was writing, I love you all for understanding. To my precious jewel, my sister, my rock, I know I drive you nuts, but you know you're all I got! A safe wouldn't be strong enough to protect you, so I will keep you close to my heart. I love you, and I thank you for helping me shape my life. You taught me everything I needed to become a man. All the people that became a true fan of my blog and my book, the people who helped mold this project into its purest form, I'm forever indebted to your loyalty. Thank you all for your contribution.

"If you don't believe in yourself, why should anybody else?"-

CHAPTER ONE

I don't know which part I hated the most, transit or going to court. I hated the entire process. We were housed in a building 24/7, and the only exposure to the outdoors was a back patio surrounded by walls. I heard the guard say the bus count was forty-five. They loaded us up into the holding cell in Miami FDC, a holdover facility. It was cramped, packed from front to back, with different shades of men from all over the world.

Some who knew each other spoke loudly as if they hadn't seen each other for years. Others like myself were silent, the reality of their fate finally settling in. My daughter Kiki had just turned ten months old, and I was about five hundred miles away. This prison shit was for birds. I was happy they gave me the lower end of sentencing, which was a hundred and eighty months. As much as it hurt me to be shipped off to South Carolina, I was ready to go.

"Five minutes till we get there, fellas," the guard yelled in his southern accent.

I sat in the middle row, feeling claustrophobic. For a big-ass bus, it seemed like a tight little space when you're in handcuffs and leg shackles. The entire ride from Miami to South Carolina took at least nine hours, between stopping for gas, and the bus driver falling asleep, damn near crashing. The long roads gleamed bright as the morning sun off the Red Maples and Sweetgum trees on the side of the highway. I finally had a view worth looking at. For the past six months, I was stuck in a unit where the windows were foggy, making it hard to see through. I badly wanted to feel the sun on my back and the wind on my face. Somewhere deep down inside, I was scared. This was my first time going to prison. Even though I prepared myself mentally for it, my stomach was tied in knots. I was going to a medium-security prison where I heard that politics weren't as bad as penitentiaries. The prison world lives by its own rules. It seemed like every ex-con I spoke to have a story to tell, regardless of where they served their time.

"Hey, Jinky," I said.

He slept soundly while the bus seemed to run over road bumps on purpose. I had to push Jinky's head to the other side when he ended up resting on my shoulder. We had long conversations from time to time on the way there, but old Jinky was tired, or maybe I was anxious. While he slept, I took in the scenery.

"Jinky, wake up my nigga," I said again, struggling to get him to hear me.

"What's up bro," he said groggily with a small spit bubble on the side of his mouth. His dreads hung loosely on top of his head as he shook himself awake.

"I'm about to call the guard. I need to use the restroom. I know you were asleep, but I need them to take the cuffs off right quickly."

"Alright." He said, yawning and putting his head back down. "Where are we at bro?" he asked with his eyes closed.

"We are in Carolina, about five miles from the spot. I got to piss like a motherfucker. It's gonna take them forever to get us situated. I might as well go now."

I signaled to the guard who sat in the passenger seat, letting him know I needed to use the restroom. He told us only to wave our arms if we had to use the restroom or was close to death. Other than that, he didn't want us to fuck with him. As he walked towards me, my mind drifted towards freedom.

He opened the safety gate that separated the inmates from the guards. Walking down the aisle, he counted each inmate, making sure nobody escaped. He only made it past the first few seats when someone jumped up, knocking him over with something in their hand. He jumped on top of the guard, not giving him a chance to make a sound. Holding the object in both hands, he swung down on him forcefully, seeming like a mad man destined to kill quickly. The driver didn't look back once. It seemed like nobody noticed it.

Am I the only person seeing this?

The prisoner grabbed something from the lifeless officer. I could see it was a gun. The prisoner got up slowly and walked toward the front of the bus through the open gate that separated the inmates. When he was satisfied with his distance, he pointed the gun directly at the driver's head. He looked back, staring me right in the eyes. Suddenly I could no longer see it. It was like a big red blur mixed with sunlight. Then I slipped back into reality.

"Hey, you! Hurry up, boy. What the hell is wrong with you?" the guard yelled in my ear.

"Damn!" I said to myself. *If I keep daydreaming like this, I'll go crazy.*

Old Jinky was staring at me intently, trying to figure out what was wrong with me. I waited as the guard freed the leg shackles from my legs. I got up, squeezing myself through the tiny space where we sat. Walking down the aisle, my eyes fell on a few niggas I knew from the holdover. Others I acknowledged out of respect.

"Number one or number two?' the guard asked as I got to the back of the bus.

He had to unlock a cage where the toilet was. When I looked at the hole in the tank covered in brown stains, I replied quickly, "I just need to piss."

The smell that came up from the tank slapped me in the nose. It smelled unnatural. I choked slightly, trying my best not to inhale too much of it. After I stepped in, this man dared to lock me in the gate. He stood guard while I tried to relieve myself. Nothing! Nothing came out. I tried my best to concentrate on something other than that stank-ass hole. I closed my eyes, I looked up, prayed, and still, nothing came out.

"Hurry up, champ," the guard said.

When I looked back, he was smiling at me. I shook myself off even though nothing came out. My bladder felt as if it was going to explode. I hadn't eaten the baloney sandwich or drank the fruit punch they passed out during the field trip from hell.

"We're here, fellas. Welcome to Estill," the driver bellowed.

When I was finally seated, I prayed I made it through this shit. Anxious, I looked out the window, trying to read the sign out of the prison gate. The bus moved slowly, circling the parking lot. I noticed an SUV pulled up on the side of the entrance on the other side. The sign on the building read *Estill Correctional Institute Medium-High*. Confused, I wondered what they meant by *high*.

The landscape out front was professionally laid out. Perfectly trimmed grass, perfect trees, perfect shrubs, it was all in taste. Even the white paint on the walls outside the buildings was fresh. I expected Count Dracula's castle with paint chipped, dark gray walls. A guard came down the aisle, asking each of us one by one our name and registration number. After he was done, another guard came down the aisle, pulling people off the bus. Before they got to the middle where I was sitting, I noticed a separate cage from where we sat upfront. I must have missed it when I first got on the bus.

Two guards walked up to the gate, one holding a separate set of keys in hand. The guard that opened the gate helped a white man get out who sat alone in the cage. He must have been at least six-foot-six and had to weigh over two hundred and fifty pounds of muscle.

"Looks like I'm the only cracker in the box, huh?" he snarled loudly and looked around.

His chest stood out in front of him like another little person. His whole head was covered in tattoos. When he turned around to leave, I noticed a big red swastika tattooed on the back of his head. Then he was led off the bus alone, separate from all the other inmates. Now I know why he sat alone.

"Name and number? Inmate," a guard spoke after he loosened the leg shackles.

My ankles were sore to the bone, but I managed to get out of the seat when he instructed me to. He still left the cuffs around my wrists.

"Mahkahi Guierra, number three-zero-five-seven-eight, dash zero-zero-four," I replied. The guard then led me off the bus into the South Carolina humid summer.

The air was muggy, and the sun I desperately needed felt like a hot rag on the side of my face. Leaning back, I cracked my chest, then twisted my neck from side to side to get my spine aligned. Sitting in one position for so long had made my entire body stiff.

The next couple of hours were as intense as going through transit. We did the same processing we did at the other institution; fingerprints, photographs, and moving from one holding cell to another. We were fed another round of baloney sandwiches and jungle juice. Finally, we were taken to where we were going to be housed. All of us separated, including old Jinky, who stayed quiet the whole time.

"Guierra." a light-skinned woman yelled.

"Yeah?" I replied.

"Come on," she said, opening the cell door.

I followed the woman into a small room about the size of a bathroom. A table sat in the middle of the room with two chairs on both ends. She asked me to have a seat. I sat quietly, watching her as she looked inside a brown folder that was already on the table. She was a beautiful woman who appeared to be biracial, probably with one white parent and the other black.

Her black side dominated her genes. She wore a tight-fitted Aeropostale shirt that cupped her breast perfectly, with some Aeropostale jeans that fit her five-foot-five, curvaceous, coke bottle frame. Her feet were tiny, which complements her petite figure. She was sporting some all-white Air Force shoes. A single necklace hung around her neck, and a black Movado watch hugged her wrist.

She wasn't dressed like her co-workers. She must have been a social worker or something, I thought to myself. I liked the way she had her hair pulled back into a tight bun. It was curly and slicked back, making her edges wavy. She was someone I would fuck with on the streets. Finally, she spoke.

"I'm Ms. Calder, a counselor here at Estill. Consider this orientation, plus I have to find a placement for you," she said, smiling at me and staring me into a trance with her dark grey eyes. "What's your name and registration number?" she asked.

"Mahkahi Guierra, number three-zero-five-seven-eight dash zero-zero-four," I repeated.

"Is that your full name, Mr. Guierra?" she asked while writing something in the folder.

"Yes, that's my full name, Ms. Calder," I answered.

The temperature in the room didn't seem to faze her. I, on the other hand, was as cold as hell. I tried my best to stay warm by keeping my legs stretched and crossed out in front of me, and my arms crossed on my chest. That shit wasn't working. It was still freezing.

"Damn, it's cold here," I said out loud.

She didn't respond.

"Take your shirt off," she demanded, writing something in her folder and never looked up.

I noticed a smirk on the side of her face.

"What?" I said, surprised.

"Again, take your shirt off, Mr. Guierra," she said without explanation.

I had to look around the room. There were no cameras and no windows that anyone could look into, and the door was closed.

This broad tripping.

I replayed her request in my head for a moment before finally doing what I was told.

"How many tattoos do you have, Mr. Guierra?" she asked without looking up.

"I lost count," I told her dryly.

Tattoos covered my arms, chest, neck, left leg, and back. Ms. Calder looked up at me, curiously, reading my body. I loved it when women did that. Sasha, my ex-girlfriend, told me once that my tattoos were like a book. They told a story that only I could tell from the beginning to the end.

"Turn around," she said, holding her pen under her chin.

I could see the curiosity in her eyes as she stared at me, seemingly interested. She was reading me.

"How long have you been getting these done?" she questioned, pointing her pen at my body.

"Probably since middle school," I told her.

She nodded, satisfied.

"Ok, you can put your shirt back on. I'm just going to put full-body tattoos on here," she said, shaking her head. "Are you in a gang?"

"A gang? Nah," I laughed.

"So, you're not in a gang? You have flames around the word Zoe on your forearm and five, five-point stars from your neck to your shoulder blade. Do you know what red flames and five-point stars represent, Mr. Guierra?" she continued.

"I don't know what they represent to you or anybody else, but I know what they mean to me," I said, looking through her soft eyes.

She made slits with her eyes. I felt like she was playing games with me now; it was hard to read.

"The Bloods and Crips are on this compound, more Bloods than Crips. Both have enemies. I can't help you if you can't identify your set."

"My tattoos represent the footwork that I put in, Ms. Calder. It's my life story; I didn't have time to write a book. The five stars just mean that I'm a General, at least in my hood. There aren't any gangs where I'm from. We take charge. Nobody follows a man; we learn from each other. I was born to be a leader," I explained.

"I'm interested in your story. You sound like a very smart young man," she said, putting her pen down.

"So, you gonna sit there while I tell you my whole life story?" I questioned.

"Start from the top, Mr. Guierra. As I said, I have to find you a placement, but first I have to get to know you," she stated.

CHAPTER TWO

I wasn't always inmate number three-zero-five-seven-eight dash-zero-zero-four. I didn't start here at Estill Correctional Institute. It's deeper than this little country town in South Carolina. I'm from a city that praised words like Chopper or Stick, which are slang for AK-47. If you asked the average young nigga who owned an AK-47 what it meant, or who made the shit, they probably couldn't even tell you. It's an honor where I'm from to have either owned one or died from one. Ain't that some crazy shit?

It's like this. In the game of life, you play the streets close and watch your friends closely. The real enemy could be yourself and who you're influenced by. Like in the game of chess, every piece plays a position. Foot soldiers play on the field, like pawns. They're loyal, but they're used for the same purpose as pawns, to protect and serve like what a Teflon vest does for your chest. They serve the objective of letting leaders gain more leverage. Now, it all depends on what position you feel you play in the streets because not everyone is a born leader. Some people are meant to be followers.

Believing there's a guaranteed spot in the game of life would be a gross overstatement. This life is a competitive game, and everybody's trying to get to the top. In this game, just like in chess, we have the winners, and there are the losers. No in-betweens. No one wants to lose, and everyone plays for keeps. There's one problem, though; you can lose in this game of life. It ain't like chess where you just turn the board around and trade pieces. Dead is dead! There are three types of people in the streets: the grimy, the loyal, and the two-faced. Growing up, I was always taught to keep my grass cut, so I could keep an eye out for the snakes. My cousin Uno used to say something that I held dear to my heart, and it ended up meaning more than I thought. "The good guys always finish last." He would tell me over and over, every time we crossed paths. There wasn't room for friends in the streets. You had to play that two-faced role, for keeps....

• • •

Nothing prepared me for the obstacles I had to face. My father and I would often have these boring sit-downs. In the back of our apartment, I would watch him sway back and forth in his favorite chair that he treated like a rocking chair, although it wasn't. With a half-bottle of gin in one hand and a long cigarette in the other, he was always drunk and out of his mind. The smell of alcohol used to be so strong; In fact, I can still smell it today. I can still hear his voice like an echo in the distance.

'Kahi, you have to learn how to swim with the sharks' son. Yooooou got nooooo idea,' he would slur as he sipped his gin and smoked on his cigarette simultaneously.

Though I would listen, his words were meaningless to my young ears. I was counting on him to pass out. Sometimes I felt he wanted to love us, and other times I felt he didn't understand what love was. It was confusing to me.

I grew up to despise him. He was an alcoholic who couldn't do anything right once he was drunk. When he got drunk, it was bad. He used us as his personal punching bag and treated my mother like a pair of old drums; his arms were sticks. He beat her badly so many times, I lost count. The first time I witnessed his rage, I was around four years old. I felt helpless. There wasn't much I could do. He scared me mentally to where I'll never forget it.

Standing six feet tall, one hundred and eighty pounds, my father towered over my mother's five-foot-three, petite frame. Imagine a young Ali in his prime, drunk, and stumbling around the ring; that was my father. His lean, handsome features were twisted by the booze. Our living room was a ring, and my mother was his sparring partner.

Our small living room consisted of only two second-hand leather sofas, a small TV that only showed two channels, and a small coffee table full of cigarette butts. I can still remember my mother's small frame in plain sight. I watched for the first time in my life, my mother being physically, mentally, and emotionally torn apart. I usually go and hide in the bedroom that I shared with my little sister, Kadisha. Talking about sharing a room, shit, there were times we had to share the same butter bread sandwich. Some nights I would cradle Disha into my little arms to stop her from crying. This particular time, I couldn't find her pacifier in the dark, and the light switch was too high for me to reach. Lucky for me, I kept a lollipop in my pocket for times like this.

I would listen to the drama just beyond our bedroom door, tears streaming down my face. I wore the stigma and the pain of feeling helpless and weak. I hated seeing my mother abandoned, with no one to help her. I couldn't do much to stop the abuse. If I had been older, it would have been a race to see what killed my father first: the booze, cigarettes, or me! I remember her begging him to stop and trying to calm him. My mother would mumble secretively, reminding him that we were in the house.

As abusive as my father had been, he was careful not to leave visible scars. He never hit her beautiful face, but he still broke her beautiful heart. My mother's smile was as gentle as her touch. It seemed to glow in the dark on the darkest nights. It's unnatural to go to sleep at night with that shit on your mind. But I would wake up the next morning to my mother's soft voice as if the night before had been a bad dream.

"Kahi, get up, baby," she would say gently.

As she scrubbed the bottom of my feet with a wet towel, her little soldier wanted to ask her questions badly.

Why do you take that stuff, ma?

Why do you let daddy hit you like that?

Not long after that day, he spared no one short of the same treatment.

The neighborhood added to the fucked-up mindset. Along with the abuse at home, the streets ain't offer a safer outlet. Guns, drug dealers, pimps, whores, dope fiends, and wranglers ran the block outside our steps. It seemed like the streets were their recycling bin. Every time the police snatched one up, another one would spring out the bushes. Stepping off your porch was like leaving enemy lines to encounter another. It's sad to say that seven out of ten people fell victim to the streets. That was just from my experience; I might be off one. This is the late eighties we're talking about.

The crack epidemic spread like wildfire. The Medellin Cartel painted the streets of Miami red, and I'm not talking about paint. Your lifespan in those times was short, and if you were in the streets, you might have had a forty percent chance of living. There was a fair share of injustice that plagued our city.

If a drug deal went sour, and the shooter wanted his

or her target, old lady Betty or little four-year-old Caren, weren't safe from the chopper bullets when they came spinning. Innocent people fell victim to the crime. You would think it would stop there. Making it out of the hood was one of the greatest challenges to overcome.

The stereotypes were anything but bias. Coming from where I'm from and being black only meant one of two things: death or jail. Even when a nigga did make it, there was still the stigma of growing up black, hanging over your head. How do you reap the benefits of sunshine when all you know is rain? Only a few make it to where they need to be. I'm trying to duck becoming a face on my mother's T-shirt.

CHAPTER THREE

I was hanging out with my day-one niggas: Kirby, Rah G, and Fat Boy Tre. Kirby was the type of kid who tried to get over someone by any means. His ditching school was contagious. He seemed to have an outlet no matter what the situation called for, the right plan, at the right time. We all took a liking to his way of thinking and soaked up the game along the way. This kid had a gift of gab. He could sell fire to the devil. We were in fourth grade, but he was more exposed.

He once talked to his mother into letting us stay at his house on a school day unsupervised. Of course, I knew better what happened that day and how he pulled it off.

"Ma, they just said we had to go home because they had a shooting at the front of the school," Kirby told her.

In his defense, this was a common thing in our area. His mother looked like the breath of life had been knocked out of her. She grabbed and held him tight, looking into all our faces. We all hung our heads low, trying to avoid eye contact with her. She held him to make sure he wasn't hurt and ran her fingers over his body from head to toe.

"Mrs. Isdopher said she tried to call, but nobody picked up the phone," Kirby added.

"Nobody called here, son, I was here all morning. Maybe she called when I was in the shower,' she reasoned.

"Here, mommy, she told me to give you this number. She said to go home since I only live a block away. She said if you were home, to give you this number."

He handed her a note we found on our way to his house. It was on the floor, next to this junkie named Scoot. We had him write a note with Fat Boy Tre's brother, Ghost's phone number on it, with the promise of a piece of rock for him. After finishing the note, we took off running when he was done, without paying him. She took the note and studied it for a second. In her mind, this was a hassle to deal with. She was already late for work. She knew if we were in the house, we were safe. She took the bait.

In the hood, our mothers couldn't afford to miss a day's work. If the bills didn't get paid, they oftentimes would be labeled as an unfit mother, or worse, Child Services would get involved. Kirby's mother could barely make ends meet. She couldn't stand there another minute talking to us. It was either worry about this one school day now, or risk getting chewed out by her boss.

"OK, I have to go to work. Make sure you all don't touch anything and go to Kirby's room. Do some homework or something. Make sure you all don't take your asses out that door and don't pick up the phone. I'll try to come by during my lunch break. There's milk in the refrigerator. Don't waste no cereal, and please lock this door!" she stated quickly.

Back then, that was some brave shit for us to pull, considering everybody in the hood knew each other. Whenever word got out, news spread like a disease, especially whenever shooting was the topic. *Don't fold for nothing*, was our motto. We already committed to the lie, so if we got caught, we would suffer the backlash together. We were all in.

I went to Toussaint Louverture Elementary School. It's in the heart of Little Haiti, originally Lemon City. I swear it seemed like half of the island moved to Lemon City in the early 70s when President Aristead got into power. When you're used to living on the island, you tend to migrate in groups. Little Haiti was the perfect destination to migrate to, and it became ours.

We would skip school more often during the summer classes or closer to the holidays. People were busy working or planning vacations. They hardly paid us any attention around those times of the year, and that's why it was so perfect.

Rah G was the baby boy in our eyes. He was more than a year younger than the rest of us, but he had heart. He had something to prove to us. What he was trying to prove, we never questioned, but his heart was bigger than any of ours. His obsession with numbers drove me nuts sometimes. He had big dreams of making it out of the hood and being rich.

One day I asked him, "Nigga, be for real. Who do you know left out the hood and was rich?"

"Nobody, fool. That doesn't mean I can't be the first, though," he retorted.

I thought he watched too many movies or idolized Fat Boy Tre's older brother Ghost. Ghost had all of us wanting to get money. This dude was the definition of 'shit to sugar;' the hood rich story. He went from riding a bike to becoming one of the major street dealers in the area. He was a neighborhood rock star, and I don't mean music. He was also known for his near-death experiences. This man had been shot on three different occasions and bounced back every time. He went right back to getting money like nothing ever happened.

Rah had a lot to look forward to in life. I had to give it to the kid, math was his thing. He favored school, and numbers were his gift. I couldn't understand what he was doing hanging with us. He technically wasn't from the hood. His mama lived in El Portal, where the middle-class lived. He stayed the weekends at his mom's, and the weekdays with his grandma, who lived a few blocks away from Kirby's.

Fat Boy Tre was an out of control, obese kid, who lived off junk food. He had a sweet tooth for candy or anything sweet. If he had any money, all of it would go to sweet cakes and candy. His favorite was Twinkies. He had it so bad, on top of the free lunch the school gave, Tre would con kids by pretending to sell them his tray for their snack. When they fell for his con, he used his size to take his tray back. The kid was the color of midnight, with a crooked eye. He sported a high-top fade, with a face only a mother could love. This grease ball wasn't about to share a crumb. If you ask me, he was the greediest motherfucker I'd ever met in my short time on earth. He had a dilemma and wasn't all to blame. If my mother was turning tricks in exchange for drugs, instead of putting food in the house, I would be greedy too.

That was our crew, just the four of us exposed to grimy streets at a young age. After school, the guys and I had a routine we would follow every day. We would hang out at a park that was adjacent to the elementary school. There was an apartment building across the street that turned into a trick motel and dope hole.

Everybody who was somebody in this area came through that building. Dope boys did drop-offs and pick-ups, dope fiends copped, and tricks tricked. Our meeting spot was the bleachers, next to the basketball court, a few steps away from the candy lady house. This was so Fat Boy could make his five-minute sweet runs.

"You all see Roxy? She is about to go in, ya'll," I said excitedly.

We all looked in unison, as our favorite prostitute

strutted over to a four-door car. The windows had extra dark tint, even with the sun, you couldn't see who was in the car. The driver rolled the window down just enough to say something and not be seen. Roxy loved to work on what her mother gave her. She didn't give a fuck who was watching. Her ego owned the block. She stood five-feet-eight inches with knee-high boots. The tights she wore hugged her flawlessly curved body. Her hair was cut into a mullet, short on the sides and high at the top. She had curly red hair that looked to be recently dyed. It hung freely on her back. She resembled Foxy Brown, black and beautiful.

As she walked to the passenger door, she tugged at the back of her tights that rode into her large butt cheeks. Her ass damn near fell out of those tights. I stole a glance at Fat Boy, and he was in a trance, staring at her fine-ass cheeks like they were two big Twinkies. He looked back and forth from his left to his right at each one of us.

"Damn, she is fine," he said.

He had a zebra cake in his fat hand-stuffed mouth. I shook my head at him and looked back at the prize. Shit, we were only in the fourth grade and knew what was up, or at least pretended we did.

The guy finally scored his date, the broken lights went out, and the car was rolling. Everybody that stopped by to see Roxy usually did. We watched him circle the block a few times, making sure he didn't see anything he didn't like. He parked a few buildings down. She got out first, making her way to one of the apartment doors. I made a mental note that she never went to the same door every day, but there was always one available.

The guy got out fumbling with something in the passenger seat, I guess, to make sure the doors were locked. Finally satisfied, he closed the car door and turned around. I got a good look at the dude. He was the spitting image of Willis from Different Strokes. Shit, if I didn't know better, I would think he was the child star. He was acting weird. He was peeking and looking around as if someone was following him, similar to what crackheads do around here. Roxy came back agitated like she was in a rush to get him inside. She put one hand around his waist to show him she was guiding him to her place. She easily towered over him, his hand on her right ass cheek. Anybody who wanted to see the show, it was free. Kirby was staring so hard; he didn't realize he was sliding off the bleachers where he sat. He leaned too close for comfort, and BOOM! – That's all she wrote.

"That ain't funny, my nigga!" he screamed, as the rest of us burst out laughing.

"Help me, Rah," Kirby yelled, stuck between the bleachers.

While they were tripping over what happened, my attention went back to the pair. I watched as they got to the room. It was only a two-floor building, and they were staying in the last room, the one closest to our view. She went to her bro looking for something. Before they got all the way through the door, she was already on her knees. I jumped off the bleachers screaming.

"Awwww shooooot, you all ain't see that? Awww shooooot!" I said excitedly.

"You all ain't seeing that?"

"See, man, you clumsy-ass nigga, I knew I was going to miss something fucking with your clumsy ass," Rah said disappointed.

"What did you see?" asked Fat Boy.

"Yeah, nigga, what you saw?" Rah said, looking at Kirby shaking his head.

I put on my Colgate smile and looked everybody in the eye. I was the center of attention and was loving every second of it.

"She was sucking dawg dick," I said nonchalantly.

"Oh, man," Kirby shouted.

He started dusting himself off, looking past me in Roxy's direction, hoping to catch a glimpse of something, but the door closed. Rah had this skeptical look on his face. He gave me one of those 'yeah right' looks.

"I'm serious, man, I saw it. She thought she closed the door, but it ain't closed all the way. She got on her knees, and the dude was in front of her and put his thing in her mouth. I know she wasn't cleaning the floor," I said.

I had to exaggerate a little bit. I didn't see the man put his dick in her mouth, but I know better than to think otherwise. I imagined getting my dick sucked by a fine woman like that. I got home later that afternoon with that thought in my head. I greeted my mother in the kitchen, cleaned my room, and got something to eat. After I finished my chores, I sat in front of the TV with my pops that night waiting for my mother to finish cooking.

Breaking News! Tamika Hardwell was found murdered in the Hills Homes Apartments, located on Northeast Fifty-Sixth Street. Her body was discovered at four p.m., and she was pronounced dead at the scene. Neighbors confirmed that Ms. Hardwell had strange men coming in and out of the many empty apartments. State records show Ms. Hardwell had been arrested on several occasions on drugs and prostitution charges. No details of her death can be provided at this time. If anyone has any additional information surrounding the death of Tamika Hardwell, please call Crime Stoppers.

I happened to look up, and Tamika Hardwell's mug shot from a previous arrest was on the screen. My heart almost leaped from my chest. I felt like I was going to throw up.

"Boy, why are you looking at the TV like you saw a ghost?" my dad asked.

I looked back at him; shock still visible on my face.

"Nothing," I said.

I turned quickly to listen to the rest of the story, but they had already moved on to the next story. Roxy was dead, just that quickly. I don't think Crime Stoppers know what happens to people who don't mind their business.

CHAPTER FOUR

By the mid-90s, we moved three blocks down the street from a tiny apartment. We went from Fifty-Fifth Terrace and Second Avenue to Fifty-Eight Street and First Avenue. That part of *Little Haiti* had nothing but trick hoes. Ever since Roxy was killed, everybody stopped going to the apartments, because shit got hot. They never found the person who did it. Some say it was probably one of her johns. Others say anybody could have done it. That wasn't the reason why we moved.

Traffic was booming down a well-known strip called Biscayne Boulevard. Biscayne was full of clothing stores, food markets, and different restaurants. If you had a thing for prostitutes, this was the spot. Along Biscayne, you could find men acting like women, and women willing to do whatever a man wanted for the right price.

The plan was to move to fifty-eight street to have a little peace of mind and get away from all the bullshit. Fifty-Fifth Terrace, where I used to live, was rumored to have zombies walking the blocks late at night. I think crack heads were stealing, and trying to find a place to smoke, and may have appeared to people as zombies. But hey, what the fuck do I know? In Haitian culture, to ward off evil, voodoo was commonly used. Some people believed it to be witchcraft, and I couldn't blame them.

Any time of the day, you could find chickens, pigs, and other strange shit roaming the city block. Not to mention, Haitian men and women dressed in all white and sported colorful beads as jewelry around their necks. Some people believed in soul snatching and used it at their will. Most people that hear stories about Haitians create this image that Haitian people used voodoo to harm others and nothing else.

We had a backyard with enough rooms to run, which wasn't cramped like the apartment. The house didn't have that *wow* factor, but it was home. It was better than coming down the stairwell, worrying about stepping on a broken crack pipe, open condoms, or heroin needles.

While playing in the front yard of our house, I noticed a bowling ball green, 87' Monte Carlo creeping slowly down the block. It felt as if someone hit the slow-motion button. As the car got closer, I paid more attention. The two-door had a T-top roof, with fifteen-inch Hammers and Lows rims. H & L's were the hottest at the time. The paint was dripping wet. "Snoop's *Murder Was the* Case," was blaring clear from the speakers, while the bass vibrated the ground like an earthquake.

As the car grew closer, I noticed it was Juice, with Ghost riding shotgun on his Motorola block phone. The big grey ones that said, 'I got money because I got money.' To see him riding in style like that blew my mind. May I add the Hammers and Lows hugged the car like twin sneakers? My eyes danced around the wheels as they spun to a stop in front of my house.

I craved that attention they were getting badly I needed to feel what they felt from the outside looking in. In my mind, those niggas were doing it big, and I knew ain't one of them; niggas graduated with a diploma. The only diploma them niggas had was a degree in street analysis. They had it all: cars, clothes, shoes, and more shoes. I really didn't care about school now.

Juice and Ghost were holding down parts of Little Haiti. They weren't the head niggas in charge, but their reputation still held major weight. This wasn't the first time I saw them flashy. I didn't know too many niggas that challenged them. Juice and Ghost had a 'get down or lay down' mentality. If you weren't with them, you were against them. Every now and then, you would hear about a dude who might have felt a little froggy and jumped. They were known to bust a few heads here and there, but they were smooth with it. As fast as an incident would occur, they would annihilate it without commotion.

"What's good, Jit?" Ghost asked, putting a hand on the receiver of the phone. Juice smiled, exposing a new set of gold teeth. There was so much gold, you couldn't see any white in his mouth. They shined like the sun. Just a couple of days ago, he had pearly white teeth. My heart skipped a beat because it took me a minute to respond. These niggas stopped right in front of my house, but why? I leaned in and got a closer look at the interior of the car. Each of them had a Cuban Link chain gracing their necks. They seemed like twins on a mission to look alike. The inside of the car was trimmed in gold. The seats were peanut butter-colored, and the steering wheel was gold with a start in the middle. It looked like a spaceship there.

"Nothing, what's up," I said, smiling back with a missing tooth.

Juice nudged Ghost. I could tell by the way he jerked that Ghost looked at Juice, confused. They looked past me. When I looked back, I didn't see anything. They looked at each other approvingly, then looked back at me. The music was turned down low, but I could still feel the bass knocking from the trunk.

"What are you doing outside by yourself, Jit?" Juice asked while Ghost was still on the phone.

"I ain't doing shit. I got bored in the crib, so I came out here. I really was trying to see if Ghost's brother was coming through."

"Look at this little nigga, Ghost. When I was his age, I wasn't talking like that. I respected my elders," Juice responded.

"Jit, they are off the chain. My little brother told me how you all fought in the cafeteria. Something about some food or some shit. You all tryna put down people's kids, huh?" Ghost said, putting his hand over the receiver.

"We ain't making no noise; that fool deserved that. Besides, we had to jump, fool; he was wilding out," I said.

"You are all crazy, Jit. You all need to cut that stupid shit out and get summa this paper out here. You're going to fight about something, make it about something that makes you rich. Check this out, though. A lot of crazy shit is going on out here; you shouldn't be out here solo like this. You can't get hurt fucking off and ain't shit out here," Juice said, looking in his rearview mirror.

"I ain't gonna get hurt Juice, and if I do, my daddy got a big old gun in the house. Ain't nothing going to happen to me because my daddy will shoot them," I responded.

"Check this out Jit, you better not ever go near that gun unless your daddy or mommy needs you to. Watch yourself and be careful. You are in a cage with lions, sir, you'll understand when you get older. Come get this, I'm tryna dip," Juice replied.

Juice's hand disappeared and reappeared again with a fist full of money. I undid the dangling lock in haste, praying my mother wouldn't hear me, and come out of the house. No sooner than I could get the gate open, my plan failed.

"Entre na kay-la konye a!" There was no mistaking who the voice that was. English was predominantly spoken in my house, other than when the family visited the islands. When my mother was mad, she always made her point in Creole. And when she spoke Creole, an ass whooping was nearby.

I took a step back, then another until I saw the little white line she told me to never cross unless it was an emergency, or that was my ass.

"Go ahead, Jit, get in the house. I'll give this little change to your old girl to hold for you and shit," Juice explained. Ghost's eyes were fixed on my mother as she walked to them.

"Shit no," I mumbled to myself.

Ain't no way in hell I was getting that money now. I broke the Golden Rule and crossed the little white line; she was definitely taxing my ass. I just turned around and headed for the door. On my way into the house, before I could fly past her, she popped me over the head without looking. If they knew like I knew, they would have pulled off, because mom was about to give them the business.

I went into the house and hurried to the window to see what was about to happen. I was still rubbing my head from her popping me. She stood at the gate, and it looked like they were having a normal conversation. Ghost was still on the phone, and Juice's face was serious. He mostly nodded to whatever she was saying. Ghost ended up getting out of the car and handing her my money. She tucked it in her back pocket. It was so much, she filled up her other pocket.

My mother was far from lame. She knew them, boys, from somewhere, probably through their mothers. She knew what they were up to and didn't want that life for her children. She prided herself on hard work, morals, and principles. She was a beautiful woman who was giving, optimistic, and motivated. She rarely wore make-up and carried herself with the respect of a married woman, even though she wasn't married. My father was a monster when he was drunk, but he and my mom shared that thing called *love*.

She stood by that love, no matter what, and held onto that respect for him. Some said she favored Whitney Houston. She was a very vibrant family woman. I wouldn't describe her as strict. I believe she wanted the best for us. I felt she overreacted sometimes. Who was I to have an opinion though, I was just a kid. The lady had a hell of a lot of responsibilities, and I had to respect that. When she came back into the house, she didn't say a word. She just took out her sewing machine and went to work. Usually, she would come in and start fussing.

I started to clean my room. That was my way of trying to fix the mess that I created. The silence was killing me. I walked past her into the kitchen to get a broom and dustpan. I could feel her eyes on my back as I made my way to the kitchen. I thought for a second, I have to make this right. I stood next to her while she sewed, tears coming down her eyes.

We looked at each other for a second. When she smiled, I smiled back. She took the cold glass of water I made for her, took a sip, and set it on the table, then bent down and kissed me on the forehead. She turned back to her machine without a word. My family's idea of moving into a new house took a turn for the worse, and this was the beginning of our troubles. This led to a part of my life that I wished I didn't have to relive.

CHAPTER FIVE

Icouldn't stay out of trouble even if I ducked behind a bush and shoot trouble in the head. One day, I got in trouble because of Rah G, who was my classmate. This was all because this other boy wouldn't let him borrow a pen. The boy sat next to me, and I thought the shit was funny how Rah-G cut up on the kid. Rah instigated it so much, the kid got up with tears in his eyes, and left. I was still cracking up when our science teacher Mrs. Cousins came in. The boy told on us, and Mrs. Collins dragged Rah G, the boy, and me to the principal's office.

While sitting in the principal's office, I couldn't believe how this little punk motherfucker snitched on us, not just us, but on me, of all people. He was talking about how 'we' took the pen. All I did was laugh at the soft little joker because that shit was funny to me.

Mind you, my father came to school a couple of days ago about me acting up in class. Now I was going to get an ass whooping for real, and I laughed. He straight up lied about me being involved, and when I tried to plead my case, it was to no avail. They weren't trying to hear it. Rah and I ended up getting three days of community service cleaning up the hallways for the principal. We also had to write, 'I will not take other people's property' on ten pieces of line paper.

When I got home that afternoon, my punishment at school wasn't shit compared to the punishment at home.

My parents ain't play that shit. They took turns making holes in my pants from the switch they used to whoop me.

Here I was, sitting on a pillow on my windowsill, my butt still sore from my whopping two days before. It was the weekend, and I was peeping daytime traffic on my block. I felt like my punishment was a life sentence. No TV, no playing outside, and no friends coming over. Just me and my room, which was no fun because I didn't have toys. I tried to plead my case again to my mother, who was more understanding than my father, but she wasn't trying to hear it. As much as I got in trouble, being falsely accused was still unfair.

Traffic on the block was booming. Friends were running in and out of the trap house that sat at the end of the block, like zombies chasing blood. Hoes were walking up and down the block like models on a runway, auditioning for an agency. People were everywhere.

Suddenly, shots rang out. I looked back because it sounded too close for my comfort. People were ducking and running at the same time. One chick had on heels and was running on four flats. The commotion on the street was crazy. At first glance, I couldn't tell who was running with the big ass gun through the neighbor's yard. I was locked in.

'Bloc, bloc, bloc.'

The shooter fired in the opposite direction he was running from. The closer he got; I was able to see the piece around his neck. It was Ghost. Pieces of debris flew through the window, hitting me on the side of the face and knocked me down.

"Mahkahi, get down, get down!" my mother yelled from the kitchen.

More bullets zigzagged through the house. Windows

were blown out. It looked like fireworks in my house. These niggas were having a full-blown gunfight right outside my front door. There was thick fog everywhere. I couldn't even see past my hands. I laid down, shut my eyes, and put my hands over my head, trying to shield myself from getting hit. I could hear bullets hitting the gate. People were screaming either in pain or from fear. My mother kept yelling, asking me if I was OK. I couldn't find the strength to respond to her. I was too scared to say anything. Kadisha was screaming at the top of her lungs.

A crashing noise shook the whole house.

'Bloc, bloc, bloc, paa, paa, paa.'

The shots were getting closer. My mother was screaming hysterically as if she was hit. The fear took a toll, and my body began to tremble violently. I asked God to please watch over us, and then I started to cry. I was still lying on the cold floor, my pants wet from the fluid that forced itself out of me. I could feel sweat building on my face, uncontrollably. Suddenly, someone was in the house, and I sure as hell hoped they weren't there to hurt my family.

Then as quickly as it started, the shooting stopped. I could hear Kadisha crying and my mother calling out to me. I got up from my spot and carefully opened my room door. I opened it just enough to peek out the crack. As the fog cleared, I saw bullet holes all over the walls of the house.

"Mommy," I whispered.

"Shhh, shhh," she replied through sobs.

I stood in the hall for a couple of seconds before I took any more steps. I stood still, listening. It sounded like a gurgling noise, or someone choking. I walked slowly and carefully with every step I took. Walking into the living room, I saw my mother huddled in a corner holding onto Kadisha for dear life, one hand extended to me.

There was blood all over the living room and splattered on my mother's legs. I saw smeared fingerprints, and a hand laid motionless next to her leg, balled in a fist. I panicked and ran into her outreached arm. I felt sick in my stomach. Everything I ate was on the ground next to her leg. Her soft hands made circles on my back. I threw up uncontrollably. Once I looked over at the body lying next to us, I threw up again. It seemed like the more I tried to hold back, it just kept coming, until there was nothing. The first thing I recognized was the chain, then I knew it was Ghost. He was dead.

Ghost's eye socket was torn open, with thick red blood oozing down his face. His body was riddled with bullets. I held onto my mother, shaking from the shock. Next to Ghost's body lay an AK-47. If this was death, it literally knocked our door off the hinges. Though I had never seen a dead body before, I understood it immediately after seeing that shit.

● ● ●

"So, did you see a dead body on the living room floor in your house?" Ms. Calder asked.

There was shock visible on her face. Before I could answer, she hit me with a few questions.

"How old were you when this happened, Mr. Guierra?"

"Did they find out who did this?"

"I mean, what happened?"

I took a sip of the water she brought me an hour earlier, then placed the cup down. I knew she was desperate to hear more.

"You have to let me finish the story, Ms. Calder," I told her.

"This stuff really goes down in my hood. Where I'm

from, people get killed for less, but if you let me finish, I could sum it all up for you. I mean, you want me to keep going, right?" I asked. I picked the cup of water back up for another sip. It felt like hours had gone by, and my throat was dry.

"OK, continue," she said.

• • •

Niggas always tried their best to hug the block like this shit was going to last forever. Ghost, who I admired and wanted to be like, was gone. He was committed to a game that no longer had room for him. The sirens were approaching fast. Before we knew it, police, ambulances, and the local news flooded the block.

"Excuse me, are those your children? Did you know the guy who's lying on your floor?" one reporter asked.

"Do you know if the shooting was drug-related? Can you please tell us what happened?" asked another.

"Disculpa. Me gustaría hacerte una pregunta?" a Spanish man said, holding a microphone out to my mother.

My mother looked confused and held her head down. We were led to an ambulance. The police wanted to check us out and question us about the dead body on our living room floor.

"Oh my God, Jesus, please help me. Tell me that ain't my boy. Lord, please, is that my baby, Lord? God no, God noooooo, please," Ghost's mother screamed hysterically.

Damn, the word got out fast.

Where the hell did his mother come from looking like a hot mess? Her hair was all over the place. She had on a little skirt that kept rising every time she put her arms up. Her whole business was in the streets. If I ain't know no better, I would have thought she was at work. I wanted to tell Fat Boy what I saw. I searched the crowd but didn't see him. I wanted to tell him how his brother went out like a gangster.

"Calm down lady," one cop said coldly.

Another officer, a woman with blond hair, tried to console her.

"Noooo, let me go, let me see my baby. Please let me see my son. Let me go, let me go now!" she pleaded.

It took several police officers to keep her from running to the body. After we got checked and cleared by the police and EMT's, several hours had passed, and the body was still in the house. I had heard that this was an open investigation; it was going to be a while.

My father showed up. He had been at work and must have stopped somewhere because he was supposed to be home a long time ago. I watched as one officer pointed in our direction. I could see a look of panic in dad's eyes. He held my mother's face for a long time. He saw blood on her legs. She explained to him that Ghost had been shot many times, and as he was dying, he pleaded for her help. He held onto her leg as he passed away. My dad kissed her on the cheek and slid onto the floor beside her, overwhelmed by what happened.

Four more bodies laid out in the streets. Guns were still in their hands, and shell casings were all around them. None of whom were Ghost's friends.

"These guys never had a chance. It looked like they were shooting at the guy in the house. These guys over here had handguns. The guy in the house had an assault rifle. There's another black male over there with the exact same chain as the guy who's lying in the house. We're assuming their friends are closely related. He's dead, around the corner in a car with some other guy," one officer reported.

"So, what's the story with the guys around the corner? Where do they fit into all this?" the rookie wanted to know.

"Don't really know yet, rookie. It looks like something out of a movie. I can only speculate. It had to go down in that car or around that area somewhere. Whatever they had going on, they disagreed. The guy with the assault rifle kills the guy in the car, sitting next to his friend. His friend gets shot by someone else because the wounds aren't consistent with the guns on any of our other dead guys. That person is still at large. Those three on the floor gave chase and must have had time to let off a few shots. A chase ensues after the guy with the rifle must have got them a few times before he went all out. He ran over there and kicked that door down and went Tony Montana on their asses. He lit them up pretty decent before he died from his injuries," the officer concluded.

"Some balls that guy had. Dude, why haven't you made detective yet?" the rookie asked curiously.

"Don't have time for the questions, rookie. Get a pen and paper. I need you to get us a few coffees. Ask the fellas what they would like and get us some donuts on the side."

CHAPTER SIX

Ever since Ghost was killed, shit went downhill for his family. It had been a couple of months, and people were still suffering from the loss, especially Fat Boy. Fat Boy wasn't the same obese kid we hated to love. He lost at least fifty pounds in the few months after Ghost's death. Fat Boy didn't talk about what happened or what went on at home, but it was obvious. His mother became addicted to a new drug, heroin crack.

She was hoeing at an all-time high to support her habit and took on some dude as her pimp. I watched her walk by my house like she didn't see the memorial in front made by family and friends for Ghost. Her attitude was, "fuck the world." She lost herself a long time ago. When you compare the woman, she is now with the one she was when her son got killed, you would think they were two different people. I wanted to ask Fat Boy, where his daddy was when he surprised me one day.

"Megaman, what are you doing after school, bro?" Fat boy asked, stopping me in the school hallway.

I was trying to catch up with a white girl named Tabitha. I had a crush on her since second grade, and she was playing hard to get.

"I'm trying to talk to Tabitha, but you are cock blocking me right now," I said, watching Tabitha slip away.

"Shit, what's up, Fat Boy?"

"Nothing, fool. I'll just catch up with you later. You look like you are busy," he said, looking disappointed.

"Nah, fuck it, bro. She got away, anyway. Bro, I have been trying to see if she wants to be my girlfriend, but she acts like she doesn't want to give a nigga a chance. I don't know, bro; she is giving me a hard time. Look at me, I'm fresh, broke, but fresh. She's going to miss out," I said confidently.

"That's how you feel, huh? I don't know dawg, let me take a good look at you, I might be able to figure it out. I know what it is, bro!"

"Get the hell out of here. What do you know? What do you think it is?" I asked.

"It might be your stank-ass breath or nigga, you black, as in Negro black, stupid motherfucker. I ain't never seen that girl with no black people like that," he joked.

We both busted out, laughing.

"Ain't nobody blacker than you, player. Nigga, you are so black, at night, your mama had to tie a glow stick on your neck, so she doesn't lose your ass," I told him.

"Nigga, I know you ain't talking, you are so ugly your mama tried to sell you when you were a baby and they Fed Ex'd your ass back home and told her to keep the extra money."

Kirby walked up with a confused look on his face. We were laughing at our own jokes. I ain't seen Fat Boy happy like this in a minute. I missed this side of him.

"What the fuck are you all laughing at? What's so funny?" he asked.

"Your face looking like shit on a Sunday morning after breakfast," Fat Boy joked.

Kirby lunged at Fat Boy, putting him in a headlock, pretending to hit him over the head. Fat Boy could have easily overpowered him, even with weight loss, Fat Boy was still as strong as hell.

"Yo, you all quit before one of these hall monitors books us," I said.

"Fat, what's on your mind, fool? I'm about to go to class in a minute. Mr. Crush said if I miss another class, he will call my mom. I ain't having that," I said.

"Don't trip, Megaman. I'll holla at you at the spot after school. You said you ain't got nothing going on, right?"

"Nah, I ain't got nothing, just get at me. Kirby where's your lil bro at? I ain't seen him all day."

"Are you talking about Rah? He's good. He had a doctor's appointment. Probably getting checked up for that thing that's been going around," Kirby responded.

"Yeah, what's that?"

"Fuck-out-my-business-syndrome," Kirby laughed.

I shook my head. That boy was something else. We went our separate ways. I walked into class and pulled out a piece of paper and a pencil, getting ready to copy the notes from the board. Tabitha came in and sat next to me, smiling, but not looking at me. I had a thing for her, and she knew it. I had to find bait to hook this girl. I wanted to make the most popular white girl in school, my girlfriend. In the meantime, I was wondering what Fat Boy had to talk to me about. After school, we ended up meeting at the bleachers, only three deep. Rah never showed up.

"Rah, probably still with his old girl, huh?" Kirby questioned no one in particular.

I shrugged my shoulders. Fat Boy did the same while Kirby continued to talk.

"It's dead around here, though. I ain't seen nobody round the apartments since that stuff happened. Fat Boy, what's up with you, though, bro? You've fallen off and shit. You look a little thin, bro. Ever since Ghost died, my nigga you ain't been yourself."

Why did he say that? I thought to myself. Sometimes, Kirby says what he feels in his heart, and today wasn't the right time. I watched Fat Boy's whole attitude change. He dropped his head and went silent for a few seconds. Then looked in the distance and spoke his mind.

"I know, dawg, this whole thing messed me up. I felt bad for Megaman and Nem because they killed Ghost in front of his house, scaring his people and shit. I ain't never lost nobody before. Sometimes I don't know how to feel."

The three of us sat silent for a moment.

"My mother on that other shit now. She is losing her mind when she doesn't get her to fix it. People acting like they were trying to help out with the funeral and shit. But then niggas who my brother was down with, who he was loyal to, weren't anywhere to be found. Lil Joe, Juice's little brother, footed the whole bill for my brother's funeral. It's fucked up, my nigga."

He looked at both of us with tears in his eyes. This was the first time I ever saw Fat Boy cry. For a second, the whole scene replayed in my mind how Ghost laid dead on the floor, bloody. His mother was still out there selling herself to men and chasing a high.

"I'm saying Fat Boy, who is taking care of you now since Ghost is gone? It ain't no secret you're old girl doesn't know how to do right, so I know she still ain't taking care of you right now," I asked.

"Nobody fool, I have been doing me. That's why I wanted to holla at you, Megaman," Fat Boy replied.

"Why you ain't holla at me, nigga?" Kirby asked.

"I don't know, Kirby. We all know you like to lie your way through everything. I'm tryna get a straight answer," was Fat Boy's reply.

Kirby sat in silence, feeling some type of way.

"Anyways, I pressed my mom a few months ago about who my daddy was. I told her that I needed to know where he was. She told me where and wished me luck about finding him. I wanted you to go with me to see him, Megaman. He ain't even come to Ghost funeral, he ain't called or nothing. I'm down to my last, and I don't know what to do."

"Your last? You act like you've been paying bills or something. Hell, you're talking about your last?" I said

"I found a stash Ghost had and some money, about five G's. My mom stole some of it out of my pocket, lucky thing I ain't have it all in one place. That's how I have been getting by. After Ghost died, a whole bunch of niggas came to the house tryna find that stash, playing like I was stupid or something. I left the guns where they were at, so they could take that shit out of the house, but I got all the other shit."

"What other shit are you talking about?" Kirby said.

"Yeah, nigga, what other shit?" I repeated.

He went in his sock and pulled out a clear packet that had a few rocks in it and handed it to Kirby. Kirby poured a few in his hand and gave me the rest of the bag.

"What the fuck is this?" I said.

I knew damn well what it was, but I didn't want to believe I was holding that stuff in my hand.

"That's that shit that got my old girl fucked up now. Bodaz! It's a crack nigga. I really don't know how to get rid of that shit. I just held on to it till it was the right time. I got a whole bag and a half full of that shit, and a whole bag of powder. I used to watch Ghost; God bless his soul. He would cook it, but I ain't tryna do all that. He called the powder stuff *girl* and the rock stuff *Bodaz*," Fat Boy said.

He reached in his pocket and pulled out a knot with nothing but dollar bills.

"I got this and a little more in my stash at the house," he said.

He peeled off a few dollars and gave it to Kirby and me, then separated a few dollars for Rah G.

"I got an idea, let me get that bag again," I said.

I took out five rocks and put them on a piece of paper.

"Let's go by the store right quick."

Scoot was laid up against a wall nodding on the side of the store. I kicked his foot, knowing he'd probably spaz out if he saw us again, but I had that *get right* to calm his ass down.

"Huh? Nigga, fuck you kick me for? I should get up and whoop your ass," Scoot said, wiping drool out the side of his mouth.

"Man shut up baser. Here, this is what we owe you nigga and some," I said.

"Oh, you decided to come back. Huh? Let me see what I'm working with," Scoot said.

He ran the paper through his fingers. Satisfied, he opened it.

"Dayummm. This is about butter, Jit. Where the fuck do you get this from? I ain't seen no shit like this since young Juice and what's his name got killed."

"I got more. Tell your people that dope is called Ghost Juice," I said. I don't know where it came from, but the words just rolled off my tongue.

"If they want that Ghost Juice, come to the bleachers on Fifty-Sixth. We would be there all afternoon after school let us out. If I ain't there, they are there," I said, pointing to Kirby and Fat Boy.

"My other partner is gone right now. He is the one who pushed your ass down the last time we saw your stank ass."

"These look like twenty pieces. That's a lot for a

panhandler like myself, Jit. You might have to buss them down to five and ten pieces," he said honestly.

Shit, I ain't know what size this was worth or what they cost. I just threw the stuff out there. Scoot had just taught me a valuable piece of the game and didn't even realize it.

"How about you gimme all the dope you have, I sell it for you, and bring you all the money back, and you just break me off, Jit?" Scoot said.

"How about I tell my friends over here to hold you down, and I cut out your tongue for saying some stupid shit like that. I'm young Scoot, not stupid. Just young. How about this? For every person you bring with you around here, I'll give you one for yourself. Deal?"

"Deal," Scoot agreed.

I explained to Fat Boy that this wasn't rocket science, it was simple math. Scoot told us what to sell the rocks for. At first, all the rocks we had were the exact same size; twenties. After talking to Scoot, we knew we needed to cut them in half. Based on the texture of the rock, a simple pen or razor would do the trick. We could keep a few on us until we sold out. Then we would figure out the rest. When Rah came back around, we ran the plan by him, and he agreed. He even came up with the perfect sales pitch.

"Get your Ghost Juice, Bodaz, for your shoulders," Rah would yell.

"Get it and go."

Fat Boy decided that looking for his father was a waste of time. He was now more interested in getting his money up. Soon as we gave Scoot the script, the rest became a movie. Traffic came by the dozens. We had a route and took advantage of it. I learned quickly, and so did my little team. Hiding what we did prove to be difficult. We found out that crack heads were not just crackheads.

They had different talents that we utilized. Rah G kept the books with his math skills. No matter how bad we wanted to keep things on the low, our names ended up ringing bells all over the hood. Then the goons started lurking, and the police got hot on our trail. The moral of the story is, all good things must come to an end.

CHAPTER SEVEN

All the girls envied white girl Tabitha. I found out she wasn't even fully white; her pale skin made her appear to be. She moved to Little Haiti from Alabama when we were in second grade. Her mother made a living carpooling kids to school for a fee. We were talking about parents one day when she told me she was mixed. Her mom was of Swiss descent, and her dad, who was Puerto Rican, migrated to Alabama.

She also told me her dad had recently come back into her life. He had been in prison during most of her childhood for dealing drugs. They moved from Alabama to Miami because her mom always dreamed of living in Florida.

What I liked about Tabitha, was even though she was a blond-haired, blue-eyed, white girl, she had swag. She didn't try to be like other girls her age; she was herself. Normally, other white kids who went to school with us tended to mimic our style. It was something about a white kid that grew up in the hood. They talked like us and dressed like us, but not Tabitha. After convincing Tabitha that I was the boyfriend she needed, we became an item. That made a lot of girls jealous, but it came with the territory.

"Boy, I need to leave before the bell rings. I can't get any more detention slips. I already went to detention twice, messing with you. And you know my mama is starting to ask me why I keep getting detention," Tabitha said.

"Come on, TaTa, just five more minutes; I was just getting started," I said, kissing her on the lips.

"Ta girl, are you gonna sit up there with Megaman all day? We got to go, girl. I don't want to keep hearing you two smacking," her friend Tica yelled through the crack in the gym door.

We had the gym on lock from one to two in the afternoon every day. The gym teachers had a meeting at that time, and that's all I needed. I paid Tica to watch the door, so I could do my thing.

"Close that door girl, I got five dollars for a couple more minutes. Just watch the door," I said.

"You all hurry up then. God-lee man! You all make me sick with that lovey-dovey stuff," Tica whined.

"That's all. We got five more minutes. Boy, you are so crazy. Are you trying to get us caught? I ain't trying to get in no more trouble, Megaman," Tabitha said pleading.

"I ain't either," I said. "That's why you just need to give me a kiss because I'm about fixing to get in some real trouble."

I quickly reached down her shirt and touched her small breast after mocking her.

"Stop playing Megaman, you are crazy. You can't do that," she said.

"That's because you make me crazy. Now stop acting like you ain't like that," I told her, then kissed her on the lips until she stopped me and pushed me back.

"Alright, for real this time. I'll let you touch my friends one more time, but you have to hurry up because I've got to go," Tabitha said, putting both my hands on her small breast.

I really didn't know what the hell I was doing, but being the Curious George that I was, anything new to me was worth trying. I reached down her shirt again, this time pulling her small breast from her training bra. Her skin was pale, but that didn't stop me from admiring her body. She was well developed for her age. She made me feel some type of way, and I wanted more. She pushed them back into her bra, got up, kissed me on the forehead, and walked away. When she got to the door, she blew me a kiss, then winked at me.

Fat Boy transformed himself. Being greedy and bullying other kids was a thing of the past. He managed to keep the weight off and grew a few inches taller. His gear got tight, and he made a few new friends. One of those friends I couldn't stand.

Pale was from across Biscayne and had been at school for a few months. There was something about him that rubbed me the wrong way. We barely spoke at school, and he only acknowledged Fat Boy out of the group when we were around. That shit was starting to tick me off. Fat Boy took him in like a little brother, even giving him some game and a few rocks so he could learn to hustle. I had a 'no new friends' mentality. We were all we needed in the crew: loyalty, respect, and honor. Three of the most important rules of the game Scoot taught us. Fat Boy didn't see it that way. He said the kid was harmless, and I was tripping. I had Rah and Kirby pull up on Fat Boy a few times, but he avoided them and was always busy. Nobody seemed to care about the change in Fat Boy but me.

Collectively, we were able to save five thousand and four hundred dollars in cash. Fat Boy kept it at his house for safekeeping. Rah kept the books on paper, making sure we split an even amount of money and put away what we needed to be saved in the stash. It's not like I was spending a lot. If my father and mother knew what I was doing, I wouldn't make it to my own funeral.

I wasn't worried about making money like they were.

We had been hustling for a few months and made good for ourselves. Scoot was giving me something more valuable than money.

He was giving me life lessons. We spent long days after school and on the bleachers. Life was taking a toll on me. Half the time, I was too tired at school. I knew I had no choice but to stay up. I didn't want any trouble at home. Scoot taught me how to cook the powder but said never to show anybody until it was time.

He told me to observe my surroundings first because you had to put life to the test sometimes. He told me there were three things I should always remember. First, never let your right hand know what your left hand was doing. Second, the product always sells itself if I market it correctly. Third, don't work for money, make money work for you.

"I gave you this game Jit, the way life works. It ain't about how much money you can make, niggas get rich and go broke all the time. It's about longevity. Niggas nowadays live today. Make it all now and spend it all now, like they know tomorrow is promised. When you make that cash, you make it make you some more cash. You find something on the side that's not going to get you in jail, and invest in that — you feel me? Make money make you more money," Scoot would say.

He would tell me this every time we were alone. I was starting to think Scoot was tripping off that shit, but he was right. I decided to make him my silent partner. I would break him off pocket change in exchange for him dropping knowledge.

"This shit ain't free, son; you have to pay homage to the big homies. Sometimes you have to pay your dues when it's not even necessary, but that's how you get ahead in life," Scoot would say while stuffing the money I gave him in his pockets.

"OK, class, I have a few problems on the board. Who would like to go up and show us how you solve these problems?" my teacher asked while scanning the room. "So, nobody's going to volunteer? I guess I'm going to have to pick someone to come up."

"Please don't pick me up, please. Don't pick me," I mumbled to myself.

"Gregory, would you like to get up here and try?"

I looked back, and Rah had his head down sleeping. Rah was a fifth grader taking sixth-grade math classes. He slept most of the time, but that didn't affect his grades.

"Nah, I'll pass," he replied groggily.

"OK, Gregory, you'll just have to explain to your mother why you were sleeping in my class."

"Come on, man. Alright, alright. Can we make a bet then?" Rah asked.

"A bet? Gregory, are you serious?" The teacher replied.

"As sure as I know, a bird can doo-doo in mid-flight," he said sarcastically.

The entire class bussed out laughing.

"OK, this will be fun. Shoot yourself. And what is this bet you speak of?" she asked.

"There's only what, three or four months left this year, right? If I answer all three problems, can you not bother me for the rest of this year? Unless, of course, my grades slip in your class. And if you win, whatever you want, I ain't tripping," He looked her straight in the eyes.

When she didn't answer right away, he just walked up to the board, grabbed the marker dangling out of her hand, and began to solve the problems:

1) *What is the denominator of fifteen hundred and sixty if the quotient is one thirty?* "Twelve."

2) *Rewrite the decimal number forty-nine point five into a mixed number.* "Forty-nine and one-half."

3) *Four times X plus twelve is 28. What is the value of X?* "Four."

"Very impressive," she said. "Now I'm going to try you with a bonus question. Are you willing to try it? But if you get it wrong, you have to stand for the rest of the class."

"Try me," Rah shrugged.

She stood there with the marker in her hand, trying to think of something tricky. She wanted to win so badly, and she couldn't believe she was being outsmarted by a fifth grader.

"OK," she said. "What are the three degrees of measure in an equilateral triangle?"

She handed him the marker, but he didn't take it. He just looked, first at her, then at the class.

"Each angle of measure in an equilateral triangle is sixty degrees, ma'am," he answered.

She paused for a moment and just stared at him.

"That's right," she said finally.

The entire class started to clap; some even stood to give an ovation. They were just as tired as Rah was of this lady thinking inner-city kids were dumb. Rah was unfazed by the attention and walked back to his seat, yawning. The teacher's eyes grew big. She looked around the classroom to see if she'd written the answers down somewhere, and Rah saw them. Maybe someone had a calculator and was helping him. The quickness of his answers left her wondering.

"Settle down," she screamed.

"That's enough."

"How did you do that so fast, Gregory," she asked with a fake smile.

"Look, this is what I do. This is what I love. Just because my head is down, doesn't mean I'm not paying attention. I'm always paying attention, trust me," he said.

He touched the left side of his nose. He was referring to the white powder residue she had caked up on the inside of her left nostril.

"Can I sit down now?" Rah asked.

"Yes, you may. Excuse me class for just a second," she said, leaving out in a hurry.

When Rah came down the aisle, I gave him a high-five.

"Trevois Clemente, please report to the principal's office, now!" the voice said over the loudspeaker.

What the fuck they calling Fat Boy for?

Rah and I turned and looked at each other.

When our teacher returned, I asked, "Can I please use the restroom?"

The class had an assignment we were working on. When I looked up to ask her, she was staring at Rah. I couldn't tell if she was mad or confused. I was the only one who noticed.

"Excuse me, ma'am," I called again.

"Yes, yes, sorry," she said nicely.

It was the nicest I had ever heard her sound. I walked out of the class in haste. I caught Fat Boy in the hallway walking with his head down on the way to the principal's office.

"What's good, bro? What the fuck are they calling you to the principal's office for? I had to tell the teacher I needed to use the restroom to catch your ass," I told him.

"I don't know, bro, they just called me all yelling and

shit, I ain't do shit. I'm about to see what they want," he said.

"Alright," I was saying.

"Excuse me. What are your names?" a voice boomed from behind us.

Our assistant Principal and two men dressed in jeans and T-shirts stood in the middle of the hallway. "You two, what are your names?" she asked again impatiently.

Fat Boy and I just looked at each other. I was thinking the same thing he was thinking, but neither of us made a break for the exit door.

"Guierra," I answered.

"Clemente," Fat Boy said.

"Guierra, get back to class this minute!" she barked. She was still coming up to the hall toward us.

"I have a hallway pass. Can I please use the restroom?" I asked.

While waiting for her answer, I did a once over of the fellas standing next to her. There was no doubt in my mind they were undercover. They smelled like the police.

"Get back in class now, sir. That's an order," she yelled.

As she got closer and closer, I backed away. I could tell this lady was mad as hell. So, I walked off slowly enough to catch what was going on.

"Is your name Trevois Clemente?" one of the men asked Fat Boy.

"Yes, sir. What happened?" he asked.

I turned in time to see the man pull a badge from under his T-shirt.

"You're under arrest for possession with intent to distribute a controlled substance. Come with us, please," he said.

He grabbed Fat Boy's arm. Fat Boy snatched his arm

back and asked the man why he was being arrested. All I could think about was getting to the other boys and telling them what was going on. For all I knew, we were next. I had faith that Fat Boy was going to keep it real with them and not tell us. Scoot told us that each man was responsible for his own actions and that you never rat on your friends.

Later we found out that Fat Boy got set up by his so-called friend, Pale. Pale was arrested for drugs, so he had an undercover buyer buy Bodaz from Fat Boy to cut a deal. I repeatedly told Fat Boy not to fuck with that dude. I knew he was fishy. We were down to our last batch of dope. We didn't know who to get more dope from, so I made it clear to slow grind it out until we found someone to buy more from.

The police did a follow-up because Fat Boy's mother refused to get him from juvenile hall. All she had to do was go pick him up. When they sent a caseworker to talk to her, she was belligerent, and they called the police out. While the police were questioning her, they noticed a bag of heroin on a table. This gave them probable cause to search the whole house. They got more than they asked for. They found everything, the rest of the drugs, and our stash. They took his mom to jail, and just like that, it was over.

CHAPTER EIGHT

It was a Friday afternoon. Disha and I sat at the dinner table, waiting for my mother to finish cooking dinner. It was now seven o'clock, and there was no word from my dad. My father always called to check in with my mom and ask what she wanted him to pick up for his meal for the night. Even though she already knew what he liked, fried pork, fried plantains, black beans, and rice were his favorite. After he dropped off the groceries, he would leave back out to chase numbers and play dominos.

He started with this new construction company called Turnberries Construction. They paid him a nice paycheck. When Fridays rolled around, he was always out and about. We all waited around and still had no phone call. This was unusual for my mother. She couldn't stay still. She kept pacing and moving around the house. Disha and I were getting hungry. My mother decided not to wait for my father and went ahead and cooked his meal with the stuff she had in the house.

She fixed Disha and me something to eat and asked me to make sure Disha ate all her food. Kadisha was growing fast and was now in second grade. She knew exactly what she wanted, and when she wanted it.

There was a frantic knock at the door that scared all of us. Ever since Ghost was killed, loud noises at the door seemed to terrify us. I followed my mother unbeknownst to her when she opened the door. Four of my father's friends were holding him up by his arms and legs. There was a trail of blood that followed as they carried him to the couch. When he left for work that morning, he was energetic, drinking his raw egg shake, and doing push-ups in the living room.

Now his body was lying there, holding on for dear life. His eyes were rolling in the back of his head. My mother stood to stare in disbelief, tears coming down her face, and both hands over her mouth. I followed them to the couch curiously. She touched him gently, saying his name, but barely able to hold her composure. I thought she was going to pass out.

This was the bloodiest scene that I've seen before. It was surreal.

"Kahi! Go get Disha and go into the room," my mother instructed.

One of my father's friends, Big Pete, said that my father was gambling at the dominos game when he got into an argument with another friend named T-Pierre. T-Pierre was a small man in stature but had a mouth and liked to talk shit. More shit than anybody I knew. Anything could set him off. He wasn't an aggressive guy; he just liked to talk shit. My father, on the other hand, was an aggressive man and challenged T-Pierre to a boxing match.

My father took the money he put down on a bet during the game and walked off talking shit. T-Pierre clapped back, causing my father to walk back and confront him. They tried to control my father, but he had been drinking and smoking. He lost his temper, and it got physical. My father ended up jumping on the little man, and he didn't hold back. Pete said he didn't know T-Pierre had a gun on him.

Before they knew it, he shot my father twice; once in his leg, and once in his back when he tried to run to his truck.

When my father couldn't move, Pete panicked because of all the different illegal activities going on there. They couldn't risk the police coming to the spot. They loaded my dad into his pickup truck and called an ambulance to our house. They were able to get there before the medics did.

Pete said my father complained about not feeling his legs. They figured this was because he lost so much blood. When he got to the house, he was still bleeding. When the ambulance got there, I recognized the two men as the same two men that treated us when Ghost died at the house. It seemed like they were the only medics assigned to this crime-infested neighborhood. They took him to the hospital with my mother by his side. She cried, her eyes red and puffy. I, on the other hand, couldn't cry, and I didn't speak. Scoot always said, sometimes you have to read life and be quiet to be heard. So, I remained silent.

Deep down inside, my mother loved this man wholeheartedly but was tired of going through this. After coming home from the hospital, there were people in and out of the house, making sure we were OK, and at the same time, being nosey. Before I fell asleep that night, I said a silent prayer, thanking God for punishing my daddy for all the abuse he put my mother through.

Three months later, my dad was sitting in his chair in the backyard. He didn't have a cigarette or a drink in his hand. He didn't say much these days, he just stared in a daze, feeling sorry for himself. He was limited to where he could move around. This house wasn't designed for someone who was in a wheelchair.

My mother had to go out and get a second job to keep up with the bills. It was hard at first, but she adjusted, alright. The government was giving her a hard time getting special care for my dad. She knew if she didn't pick up the slack, things were going to get harder than they already were. I watched her stay in good spirits some days, and other days she would break down.

My father never allowed her the freedom of learning to drive before his accident. When she finally did, he was furious. She saved enough money in a short time to buy a used car. She started to spend time away from the house. She would shop with her sisters, something she hadn't done in a long time. She came home one day to find everything on her floor. All her ornaments were knocked off the tabletops in the living room, thrown everywhere. My dad had a fit while she was out. He fell out of his chair and had to wait for someone to come home to pick him up. He smelled like urine and feces. She tried to talk to him, but he shut her out completely. She loved him with all her heart, but she was an attractive young woman and was tired of being locked down. She was determined to gain her independence, whether it was with him or without him. She was willing to take care of him, but it was proving to be difficult. He refused to respect her.

The doctors told my father that he had significant damage to the nerves in his back and spinal cord and that he would never walk again. The once handsome, well-fit man, with an ego too big to challenge, was broken into pieces. He had lost weight and had no interest in his health anymore. He had let himself go completely. His hair grew wildly on his head and face. He wouldn't eat some days and traded his solid foods for a nutrition-filled milkshake called Ensure. He was the same.

A couple of months went by, and after dealing with his ignorance, my mother said enough was enough. She called his family in New York and made arrangements for his sister to be his caretaker. My mother forfeited her rights to any money unless he wanted her to have any. My mother became a single parent, raising two children. She made another decision that moved us out of the hood for good. This was something I didn't want to face.

CHAPTER NINE

"**M**egaman, why is your old girl talking about moving?" Kirby asked.

"And how are we gonna keep in contact? You know when Fat Boy gets home, he is gonna be tripping on how you just got up and left. This shit is breaking us up. If it ain't one thing, it's another. First, Fat Boy, and now you, Megaman," Rah said.

"She already made up her mind, talking about moving around North Miami Beach. Man, ain't nothing but crackers stay around there. I don't even know how she found that house was over there," I said frustrated.

We all sat at the bleachers after school politicking. After all that happened, my mother decided we had to go. I had already spoken to Rah about what happened with my father, and word spread quickly to Kirby. He said he heard it at school, and everybody was talking about it. I was known as the kid that always had bad shit happening to him.

After a while, things got better for my mom financially, spiritually, and mentally. She got a promotion at her new job, and she had a better relationship with my father, despite all that had happened. That woman made sure she stayed loyal to him long after he'd left the house. I still wasn't alright with bailing on my friends, but what could I do?

"Ain't nobody heard anything from Fat Boy, though? I

went by fool crib, and that shit had these new people staying in it. He doesn't write or anything?" I asked.

"I know a kid who just got out of the hall, talking about Fat Boy in that shit going hard, putting niggas on their back. He was talking about how serious boot camp was. He says Fat Boy did so much fighting as a juvenile that they made him a more serious offender. Fat Boy acts like he was on a diet out here and shit. They are really gonna get that boy in shape there."

"Besides, right now, Fat Boy has a lot to think about. I'm still fucked up about how I took that hit," Kirby expressed.

"We all took a loss. Yeah, he slipped up, fucking with that rat Pale'. I tried to tell you all fools he wasn't right and shit. But you all brushed it off like I was tripping," I yelled.

"Now we're out here, Fat Boy in there, and we ain't got no more money."

Well, I still had a little money from that investment. Scoot told me to make sure I had money on the side. I employed a few kids to buy packets of candy from Walgreens. Each pack only cost me $1.25. It came with 20 pieces of candy, which I sold for fifty cents each. I made ten dollars and had a few kids working for me. I paid three dollars a pack and kept seven dollars. By the end of the week, I was good. Even though the money stopped one way, I found another hustle. This time I put my own money away.

"I'm about to move to west bubble fuck, and a nigga is not tryna be around when Fat Boy comes around. How much time does that nigga have left anyways?" I asked.

"He got another eight months left. He just went to commitment two months ago, and they sentenced him then," Rah said.

"Ain't he a first-time offender?" I asked.

"I think so, but don't ask me how that stuff works.

All I know is he did the crime, so he got to do time," Rah shrugged.

"You know I saw that boy around the store a few weeks ago. I think fools serve people around there," Rah said.

"I know you ain't talking about that nigga, Pale because we need to get that nigga for what he did to Fat Boy. I ain't seen that fool since that shit happened," I exclaimed.

"We should try on Friday because that's when I saw that nigga Pale'. He ain't see me though, but I know he has been going up to the store, you know, the one Scoot and the other base heads hang out at. But guess who I saw Pale talking to?" Rah asked.

Before we could answer him, Rah continued, "I saw him talking to Scoot. I don't know if Scoot knows Pale is a rat, but I know if he did, he probably wouldn't be around that nigga."

"Listen," I said, slapping my hands together. "We are getting fooled no matter what. We have to be smart about it, though, because he could run to the police on us. Let me holla at Scoot and give him a rundown. We are gonna set his pussy-ass up for an ass-whooping, feel me?"

Black Barbie was the opposite of the real Black Barbie. She was the ugliest hoe with the biggest butt I've ever seen in my life. It must have been her ass because it wasn't her face. On several occasions, Scoot took me to her house to show me some tricks on the stove. He showed me a few techniques for cooking girls (cocaine), but the most important lesson he taught me was eyeballing the dope. Not all dope can take the same techniques.

My first time going there, this broad came to the door in a towel. Her face was twisted, her bottom jaw went one way, and the top jaw trembled in place. She looked high as a kite and had this stupid look on her face. Her body, on the other hand, was a perfect ten. She had a caramel complexion, her hair was done, and her feet were immaculate. She smelled like perfumed soap, and when she turned around, all you could see was that ass. They told me to stay in the living room and watch TV while they went into the room to handle "bidniss," as Scoot would say. I noticed that nothing much was in the house. My mind traveled to my little apartment a few years back. I had a TV and a sofa, and that was pretty much it. There were no accessories, pictures, or anything. I could hear everything going on in their room because the volume on the TV didn't go up much. They were arguing about something for a while, and then it went quiet. A little while later, there was a thumping sound and a slapping here and there. Scoot was getting some action.

He called me in the bedroom thirty minutes later to show me why he was taking so long. He made her lay down and spread her legs like an eagle, which she didn't mind doing. She held her pussy lips at the top, spreading them, exposing her swollen clit. Her pussy was bald and looked swollen, probably from the beating it just took.

My young mind thought back to Tabitha, who would have never let me get that far in her pants, let alone smell it. Though this wasn't the first time I've ever seen pussy, this was the first time I saw it live. It was neater than the ones I've seen on my dad's porno tapes. I was ready to leave because the smell in the room had become unbearable. It was a mixture of crack, pussy, and bum, mixed in one pot.

Every couple of days, we would go to her house. He would let me listen to him fuck her. He would tell me things like, 'you are gonna get a shot of some grown woman pussy one day.' I didn't doubt him, but that was too much woman for my young ass. I talked to him about my troubles with

Tabitha and how she played hard to get every time we were alone.

"All the time in the world belongs to you, youngsters. Just be patient, you'll get a shot," he said.

He taught me a few things about women, like their soft spots, and what women liked. He told me to lick on their ears, and once even demonstrated on Black Barbie for me to see. She said it made her pussy wet. But when I tried it on Tabitha, she said her dogs licked on her like that when she came home from school. He told me to touch the back of her neck gently when I kissed her. Tabitha said it tickled. Nothing worked, so I just kissed her until our mouths dried.

When I got to Black Barbie's, the lights were out. I told Kirby and Rah I was going the next day, then I remembered what Scoot said. *Never let your left hand know what your right hand is doing.* I decided to go that same afternoon instead. Black Barbie's house was on the same route as my house anyway.

When I knocked on the door, it swung open. I remained outside and reached in to continue knocking. Only white people investigated why the door was open. I saw the result of that in movies too many times.

"Hey, baby, what brings you to me casa?" Barbie asked in her fake-ass Spanish accent.

She came to the door dressed in the same shit she came into this world in. Nothing!

"Sup Black?" I said, trying to act normal.

I stared at her nakedness. For an ugly drug addict, she wore her body like a priceless statue. I hated staring at her face, though, and I think she knew that.

"What is your cute little ass doing here? Didn't Scoot tell you, you are too young to get this pussy?" She taunted me, patting on the top of her love box, where her pubic hair had grown since the last time, I saw it.

"How about one day you teach my young ass about some pussy? I'm tired of just looking," I said, smiling.

"You are a swagged-out little nigga. I see Scoot taught you a lot. Imma suck that little dick till you pee-pee in my mouth, boy," she said, exposing her yellow stained teeth.

"Scoot in the back, come on."

I watched each butt cheek jiggle with every step she took. She had little freckles all over her body. You could see the pussy from the back, and the peach fuzz around her pussy print. She walked confidently, shoulders up, looking back at me. My eyes were fixed on her ass. She noticed I was paying attention to her walk. She even stopped on purpose, so I could run into her butt.

"Oops, sorry," she said, just before bending down.

Before I knew it, she had her hands down my pants and on my dick.

"OK little man, you're a little happy," she seductively licked her lips.

"My man," Scoot said.

He was lying in bed with a cigarette in his mouth. When we walked into the room, there was another person under the sheets, head bopping up and down.

"What are you doing here?" he asked.

What or who the fuck is that under the sheets?

"What are you doing here?" he asked again.

I remained quiet, ignoring the irritation in his voice. I kept staring at the movement under the sheets. I wanted to see who it was, but at the same time, I didn't.

"Oh, you stuck on this here?" he points to the moving sheet.

The head keeps bobbing up and down without missing a beat and making slurping sounds.

He pulled the covers back, and at first, I couldn't tell who it was, but I knew what she was doing. She looked up at me, still bopping her head up and down. She looked away and then back at me really fast. Her eyes grew big.

"Girl, he is harmless," Black Barbie said.

"That Jit right there, he is really cool. When you finish, see if you could hit him off with a little sum."

She didn't move. She didn't take Scoot out of her mouth, nor did she speak. She sat still, stuck in position, staring at me.

"Move girl, you must be tired," Black Barbie said,

Black Barbie climbed on the bed in her position.

"Girl can't make him cum quickly enough; let me get daddy right," she said, taking over.

Scoot pulled the sheets back, covering himself and Black Barbie. The girl climbed out of bed, avoiding eye contact. Standing up, she started fidgeting and playing with her hair until she finally walked away with her eyes fixed on the floor. Black Barbie was making the same slurping and sucking sounds the girl made. I think she was extra because I was there. This was too much for me. Scoot laid back down like I wasn't standing there.

These motherfuckers high as hell.

The boldness and the smell of dope were all too familiar. He stopped her in mid-stride when he noticed I was getting impatient.

"Stay there, bitch, let me holla at my little man, then I'm gonna fuck the air out of both of you bitches. That other one over there wants me to fuck her in the ass, I gotta give the bitch what she wants," Scoot said confidently. He sounded like a real live pimp. That shit was poison to my young ears.

"Hurry up, daddy," she teased, licking her ashy lips.

"Get that girl cleaned up before I get back, you hear?"

"Boy, I know you walked over here because you want something. What is it?" Scoot said.

"What's up with that nigga that's been coming by the spot hitting you and your friends off?" I spoke as if he would catch on to who I was talking about.

"Are you talking about Teflon, Jo, or that young nigga Pale who fat Boy used to be with?" he raised an eyebrow.

"The last one, Scoot. What's understood doesn't need to be explained. You taught me that, remember? Basically, I just need to see that fool A.S.A. P, I just need the time, day, and place," I said seriously.

"Come through tomorrow at the same time; as a matter of fact, he meets me around the corner from here. I'll just hit them up and tell them to meet me by the store. I have never brought him to this spot. He ain't family. Need me to let them know or are you tryna surprise them?" he asked, pounding his fist into his open hand.

"What do you think, old head? You know what time it is. I'm tryna surprise him, so let's keep it on the low," I said.

"I know youngsters, just tryna get a feel for what's to happen. Now, if you don't mind, imma go get my freak on!"

"He's a rat Scoot, he got Fat Boy fucked up. I thought you were on point," I blurted out.

He sat there for a second, contemplating his next set of words.

"I'm always on point. I knew Rah would see them" by the store because he walked that way all the time. You keep your friends close, but you also keep your enemies closer. He only hit me off with some five pieces, and that shit ain't even that good. I was waiting for you to say the word Jit.

And sorry about your daddy, I heard what happened down there at that gambling house," Scoot said.

The old man was on point. I didn't doubt that. He never once mentioned the girl being Fat Boy's mother. I knew he knew who that woman was. This was part of the game, and probably why the old man and I got along so well. Sometimes even when you see it, you don't see it. Some things are better left unsaid. Like he taught me.

CHAPTER TEN

R ah G had a stick in his hand that he found on the ground. Kirby was fussing at him because Rah wanted to kill Pale, and Kirby just wanted to fuck him up. We stood across the street from Zube's Supermarket while Scoot and his friends hung out, waiting for Pale to show up. I talked to Scoot early that morning. He caught me on my route to school and told me he set up the meeting spot for later that evening. While waiting, I saw a few niggas strolling on bikes trying to catch sales. People were shopping, and every so often, a police car would ride through patrolling the area. Scoot said Pale would be there at 4:00 p.m., but when 4:00 p.m. came, Pale didn't show up. I looked at my watch, and it was at 4:50 p.m. The nigga still wasn't there. Rah and Kirby sat lazily on the ground under the tree.

"You are all some lazy little black children," I scowled. "Ain't none of you all niggas stay on watch with a nigga for none of the fifty minutes we have been here."

"Dude might show up, just be patient, damn son," Rah said.

He was writing an algebra problem on the ground. He picked the wrong day to think numbers. I tried to read the shit but easily gave up. Kirby was leaning his back against a tree with his eyes closed.

"Where Scoot at Megaman?" Kirby asked.

"Scoot just walked back from the payphone with Fat Boy mama. They all cuddled up and shit," I lied.

That made both of them jump up. I was lying through

the smile I had on my face. You should've seen Rah and Kirby pushing me out the way to get a good look. I moved over and let them get front and center for the imaginary show.

"Where did you say they were, Megaman? I don't see them," Kirby said as his eyes swept the store.

"That nigga lying Kirby. Look, black bean pie head—ass nigga," Rah said, catching on.

I took my turn, sitting under the tree with my head back and eyes closed. I started to get hungry and tired, and it was almost time for me to go home.

"He might have lied to Scoot. That nigga ain't got no work like that to be serving Scoot back to back. Imma gives that nigga five more minutes, then imma clear it," I said.

Five minutes came and went. We ended up talking about all the stuff we wanted to do to Pale'. We agreed to make sure we stomped him out. We took turns on the post, hoping Pale' would show up.

"Imma go holla at Scoot man, you all hold up. I gotta tell this old man we are out, so he ain't gotta chill there no more."

As I crossed the street, a speeding car almost hit me. I damn near had to run to get out of the way. Not paying attention, I stuck a bird out to the unknown driver. When I turned around, I didn't see Scoot, where I saw him last. I assumed he went around back to take a piss or something. As I went around the corner, I heard people talking.

"Just give me, ah! Two, Jit."

"Nah player, give him his own and give me mine now because last time, this sucker smoked it all."

When I peeked around the corner, the crack heads were arguing. Scoot noticed me right away and gave me the eye as to say, *this him and where are your people at?* To his left,

Pale' was picking through something in his hands, while people stood impatiently around him. He didn't even notice me standing there looking at him. All kinds of thoughts ran through my mind. I was hoping Rah G and Kirby would see me go back, but I'm sure they were distracted.

A fat guy stood in front of me, blocking my view. People were behind him making a line. I was trying to see past this big motherfucker, but I couldn't see anything. We started moving forward, so this was my opportunity. I started thinking, this is where I get closer to him. I told myself when I get upon him, I'm gonna just take off and hit him where it hurts.

Pale and I locked eyes, and I had no choice but to react. One on one, I wasn't big enough to challenge this twelve-year-old kid. This was going to be the hell of a fight. I caught him in the eye with a wild right. He stumbled back hard. I must have prayed for him to fall before I hit him, but he didn't. Pale wasn't small for a twelve-year-old, but I was for eleven and a half-year-old. Lucky for me, I've been in a few scuffles. I have been beaten so many times by my father that I mastered taking a punch or two. He recovered quickly, and all the anger showed on his face as he rushed me. He didn't think twice about the dope that flew out of his hand onto the ground. All the base heads followed the trail, picking up little pieces of crack. I felt my brain shake as his fist connected with my jaw. I tried to cushion the blow by moving in the opposite direction, but he still caught me. I fell, and he was on me going all out. I was thinking to myself that I fucked up as I blocked my face with both arms.

"Yeah, fuck-boy, you thought I was soft, huh?" he screamed.

He was on top of me, hitting anything he could find

open. I did the next best thing. I balled up. I had my eyes shut in fear that he would hit me in them. Then something in my mind told me to peek. His blows felt weak and were slowing down. He was getting tired.

As he got up, I jumped up and clipped him. I hit him with my right hand, and I connected with his ear, then left to the jaw. I was trying to get him to fall. My hands started to hurt like hell. I think I hit his head too, and finally, down he went. I jumped on his ass as he jumped on me. He grabbed my thin frame in a bear hug. We rolled around on the ground like two wrestlers in a championship match. He was holding on for dear life.

"OK, kids, that's enough. You all break this shit up before somebody calls the lawman around here," Scoot said.

Scoot was trying to pull me off Pale'.

"Fuck that, imma whoop this bitch-ass nigga. Get off me, Scoot! Get off me, man!" I screamed.

I was still swinging on Pale's ass when Scoot pulled me up. Scoot finally got me up, while one of his friends was holding Pale back. Scoot held me up by my shirt.

"Snitching-ass nigga," I yelled.

More people started to gather around, and I was hoping Rah or Kirby would hear me too.

"Now, go and find your shit over there," Scoot told Pale'.

Scoot knew damn well; his friends took it all. Like a dummy, this fool Pale went looking.

I felt a wind blow past me.

Whack!

Rah G was on him like a spider monkey. He hit Pale over the head with a stick. When Pale' hit the ground, his mouth was wide open like he was yawning. He made the strangest noise I have ever heard. Kirby came through and kicked him dead in his mouth.

"Come on now, you're all gonna kill that boy if you all don't stop. That's enough now, you got what you wanted," Scoot yelled.

After a few more licks, I had to yell at them myself. Rah was going crazy with that stick. Rah took a good look at me and smiled. One of my eyes felt a little swollen, and my lip had a little dried up blood on the side. But I was alright. The three of us ended up running away before we got in trouble.

"Ah Megaman, you let that nigga get you, fool? You see how I got that nigga with that stick?" Rah said, demonstrating a baseball player hitting a ball.

"I saw it, Rah, damn you were fast! Took you all ass long enough. That nigga caught me with a mean haymaker, fool," I said, picking at my lip. "Kirby, what's good bro? What are you so quiet about?" I asked him.

"That nigga looked dead, my nigga. I wasn't tryna to kill that nigga, I was just tryna hurt him," he said.

Kirby had a worried look on his face.

"He deserved that shit. Let me find out you are getting soft," I said to Kirby.

I threw myself up at him, but he didn't say or do anything. He just gave me a blank stare. We all walked in silence for the rest of the way home. The sun had gone down, and the streetlights were on. I had to think of a lie to tell my mom. I wanted to ask Kirby, but he wasn't in the mood right now. Maybe we should have killed that motherfucker. He put my friend in jail. He committed the ultimate betrayal. He rats on him, and if you can live with that, then you have to live with what comes with it. That's what we knew. That's how we lived.

CHAPTER ELEVEN

We had to get everything out of our house by 8:00 p.m. The truck rental place only rented out their trucks for a couple of hours a day. It was already 6:00 p.m. I figured the moving shit would carry over for at least two days. My mom was already bitching about not having money for gas, and how the rental had to go back, or she would get charged. Scoot was one of the guys hired on the spot when he and a friend were walking by.

He acted like he wasn't trying to get paid. My mom offered them a little something, even though she didn't have much. He took whatever she gave him. My mom already had the back of the truck lifted. All they had to do was bring the shit out of the house and load the truck up. My mother did her share of helping. She was growing impatient because she knew the truck had to be back.

My mother didn't know I knew Scoot, or what he did. He never said a word to me when they spoke; he just did his job. She didn't know that in many ways, he was the father figure I didn't have. I was going to miss these people. Scoot, Fat Boy, Rah G, and Kirby were my second family. Kirby didn't bother to check on me, even though he knew I was moving. I knew he was still tripping on how we fucked Pale's up. I felt time healed wounds, and it was time to move on. The school was out for spring break, so Rah came to the house to help us move. Rah showed me a letter that Fat Boy wrote to him.

Sup you all

I ain't think I'll be able to survive this crazy shit. Do you know the first two weeks are straight P. T. (physical training)? They make you run, do push-ups, and pull-ups, all in one workout. You all know I ain't built for that type of shit. I got about five redirections in them for 2 weeks for bucking. First, they give you a warning, then they let you make it up with even harder exercises. Finally, they add days if you are still bucking. Some days I wanted to quit, but I ain't tryna go to prison. That's where you go if you don't complete and shit. I'm tryna to come home.

I met this nigga named Delroy, a cool-ass nigga from the way. He is Jamaican/ Philippine and stayed in North Miami. He taught me the ropes, so I'm keeping my head straight. I miss you, niggas (no homo). What's up, Kirby and Megaman? I ain't heard from my mom, man. A nigga told me she was out there wilding and shit. When I get out, imma try to get her cleaned up. She needs help. I heard how you all flipped that boy. They say he is a vegetable. I know you all love me, but daaaammmmnnnn... I'm sorry, Megaman, for not listening to you. You tried to tell a nigga some real shit. You live, and you learn, though. I look different too, I wish I could have sent a picture with this letter. I have to rock this bald head. These niggas can't cut for shit. Soon as I get out, I'm going straight to Ceazers. I only got 4 months left, my nigga. When I get back, we are on. It's all about that paper. I know niggas from everywhere, Opa-locka, Carol City, and Overtown. They are all good people. You just have to trust me—we about to blow up like the world trade, as Biggie says.

P.S. Hold the streets down, if you see my old girl tell her I want to talk to her.

After I read that letter, I felt worse for Fat Boy than when he first got locked up. The last time I saw Fat Boy's mom was when she was giving Scoot head at Black Barbie's house. Scoot was bragging about how he had to punish both of them bitches at the same damn time. She was a full-fledged heroin addict, living on the streets and ready to do anything for a hit of that needle. I had a friend tell me she propositioned him for some cash. It would hurt me in my heart to have to tell Fat Boy some shit like that. I felt better knowing I was leaving, and I planned on leaving the hood behind me.

After packing all we could in the truck, which was half of our shit inside the house, we headed North on 1-95. I rode in front with my mom, Scoot, and others rode in the back with the furniture. I knew every time we hit a bump, they felt it more. I heard them complaining about the music my mom was listening to. Disha was with Auntie Ket-Ket, the middle child of my grandma Nah. My mom was the oldest of four children. Auntie Ket-Ket was the last to come to the states from the islands. She just had a baby with my Uncle Fan-Fan. They got married and came to the states to build a family together. Disha liked to go over to my aunt to help around the house and with the baby.

The farther north we drove, the fewer apartment buildings and duplexes I saw. The exit sign read 163 Street. We took the exit and headed east. We rode down a long strip, where businesses were lined up. There was everything from restaurants to gas stations on every other block. I made a mental note to check out the video games store I saw.

The mall sat in the center of the residential area. I remember thinking, this had to be where the rich people lived. I counted at least fifteen police cars in the area. I can't remember how many exotic cars I saw. In Little Haiti, police had to be called. Riding through fifteen deep on one strip was unheard of. The only exotic cars you saw in the hood, were rented or driven by a lost tourist. The tourists better hope none of them thirsty-ass niggas saw them, or they were getting robbed.

We turned down 182nd and pulled up to the sixth house on the left. The last time I saw the house, it wasn't as nice as the house next door. Shit, it wasn't nice at all, from the outside looking in. But now, the house was freshly painted, and the driveway was repaired. It looked like a totally different house.

I stepped out of the truck and looked across the street, where I saw two little white kids playing in their yard. Their driveway was decked out with a basketball court, a garage, three cars parked in front, and a sprinkler system. I looked to my left, where I saw more white people in their driveway, cleaning their cars. I looked to my right to find more white people watering their yard. I wasn't used to seeing so many white people on one block. I had a strange feeling like we were being watched.

Whistling, Scoot acted like he never left the hood. I had to let him know he was acting like a tourist.

"Kahi, help the men put the stuff in the house, and don't carry anything heavy," my mom demanded.

"OK, Ma," I replied.

I wasn't about to help with anything. I was just trying to scope the scene.

"Hey, you, what's up, bro?"

I turned to see who was calling me bro. This little red-headed white boy ran across the street and stopped in front of me.

"My name's Jason, what's yours?" he asked.

When he smiled, he revealed a set of fruity-colored

metal braces in his mouth that ran from one end to the other. I just walked off, leaving him standing there. I wasn't feeling the friendly shit with people who just walked up to me. Where I'm from, that wasn't normal.

When I got into the house, I looked out the window. The white boy Jason had his back to me, shrugging his shoulders. He was saying something to his sister. He had this friendly ass aura about him that I wasn't used to. He couldn't have been more than ten years old. He was pudgy and goofy looking. *I don't think I can do this shit*, I thought to myself. He turned around and waved at me. I just backed away from the window. How the fuck did he even see me?

After watching Scoot and others unload the boxes and furniture into the house, I followed my mom into the kitchen as she toted a box. I looked around the kitchen in amazement. A microwave sat in between the two wooden cabinets. That shit was unheard of in Lil Haiti. A God damn microwave! We never owned one, and this house came with one. When we wanted to reheat food, we either put it in the oven or on the stovetop in a pan.

On the left side of the fridge, a water and ice dispenser sat attached on the outside. I quickly went to a box and got me a cup that was wrapped in the newspaper. I was used to broken shit that looked good, so I automatically assumed the worst. I walked up to the ice maker, and low and behold, it spat out ice so fast I almost dropped the damn cup. I took in the scene one more time, sipping on the ice-cold water provided by the very expensive refrigerator.

"Now, this is something I could get used to," I mumbled to myself.

After unpacking all the boxes and the furniture, Scoot and his friends came and sat on the stools next to me. My mother prepared for us a quick dish to show her appreciation. She cooked my favorite, smothered fish, and white grits. That shit was so good. I ate in silence while the men conversed. My mom threw in her two cents worth here and there between bites. While her back was turned, Scoot kept picking at me. I was enjoying this moment. In the back of my mind, I knew Scoot would be a thing of the past. We understood that my mom couldn't know I had a father-son type relationship with a crackhead.

"My man, your mom is fine as hell," he whispered in my ear.

I looked at his friend, who also had his eyes all over my mom. I had to admit she was a very attractive woman. Her assets were revealed with the simplest of clothes. If looks could kill, Scoot would be dead. I gave him the eye that said *nigga, you just tried me*. In my mind, I knew there was no way in hell these niggas stood a chance with her.

"Alright, Jit, my bad. I'll never disrespect you like that again," he whispered.

I wasn't going for that slick shit. I didn't say anything, I just kept eating my dinner. Scoot looked over at his friend and whispered something to him. Whatever he said made him drop his eyes back to his plate. I would never allow a nigga like Scoot to fuck with my old girl. He always told me that bitches were conniving, manipulative, and untrustworthy creatures. He told me not to ever trust a bitch. A woman, on the other hand, was to be treated like a queen. Nobody would deny my mother to be a queen.

We had to go to my old school's open house to sign me out. I found out that the middle school I was transferred to was called JFK. The bell had just rung. While my mom was in the office with the secretary filling out paperwork, I saw Tabitha. She was standing in the hallway with her arms crossed, talking to a friend.

Her wavy blonde hair was hanging down, almost to her butt, and she was wearing a sweater slightly off her shoulders. That was the new style girls were into. She happened to turn around, and we locked eyes from a distance. Her eyes were glossy, they looked like the inside of a clear blue sea. We never walked towards each other, just looked at each other. The hall monitor cleared the hallway, and Tabitha was gonna. It was an awkward moment. I could feel the hurt in her eyes. I walked back into the office and sat on the brown couch. I put my head back and thought of all the good times I had in the hood.

• • •

There was a knock at the door. Both Ms. Calder and I looked in unison. Then she looked down at her watch. Naturally, I looked up at the large white clock on the wall. Three hours had gone by, and we were deep in conversation.

"Yes, please come in," Ms. Calder said.

She forced a half a smile as the door swung open.

"Umm. Ms. Calder, we have one more intake for you to see. Do you think you'll have time to see him? Ms. "what's her face" is mad at you for having her to take all the other inmates by herself," a black guy said.

Leaning half his body weight in the doorway. He didn't look like one of those hard nose officers. He was more of a front desk type. I guess that's her face code because it wasn't my business to know who they were talking about.

"Ms. What's her face can handle the last intake. This one is a 412, I think I have to thoroughly investigate. Think you can spare me another hour, Steve?" Ms. Calder asked.

A couple of minutes before, she was caught up in my father getting shot and wore a sad expression on her face. Her demeanor changed, but forcibly. She turned around quickly, giving him her back. She quickly winked at me, pretending to do paperwork, then turned back to face him.

"It's your show boss, run it as you please. I just hope the witch doesn't bite my head off when I break the bad news."

With that, the man she called Steve closed the door. Ms. Calder sat quietly, gathering her thoughts until I interrupted them.

"What's a 412, Ms. Calder?" I asked seriously.

I tried to think where I heard it before. She looked up into my face smiling briefly like I said something funny.

"It's a label, like when you're part of a set, a gang, or at risk to the general population," she said, using her hands to make air quotations.

"It's more tedious paperwork if you claim to be a gang member. But don't worry, it just buys me more time to hear some more of your story," she said.

"Will you excuse me a second, Mr. Guierra?" she asked.

She got up without waiting for a response. I watched her like a vulture as she turned to leave, swinging her apple bottom from side to side like a runway model. Until now, I hadn't noticed the gap between her legs as she disappeared out the door.

Minutes later, Steve came back into the room. He was a slim, tall guy who wore the same uniform as every other officer: a light blue shirt, dark blue pants. While his co-workers were dressed in uniform boots, Steve had on a pair of all-black high-end, brand-named tennis shoes, one of my favorites.

"Come on," Steve said. "Ms. Calder had to run to her office. I have to put you in a holding cell really quickly until she comes back."

When we walked back into the intake hallway, everything was much more settled. People weren't walking around like chickens with their heads cut off. A bunch of inmates in orange jumpsuits lined up against a wall in the hallway. The white paint glistened like someone just wiped them all down with that shiny stuff you put on tires and dashboards. When we got to the holding cell, it was empty. When he stuck his key in the gate, the sound of metal bounced off the walls. Once he put me in the cell, the first thing I did was walk over to the toilet to relieve myself. It felt good to have a little time alone.

I was probably in the cell for fifteen minutes. I looked up, and Steve had returned to lead me back down the familiar hallway. He led me into the same room where Ms. Calder was waiting impatiently, like I was the one who left her. As I sat down, she waited until Steve left the room before she spoke. She only acknowledged his presence with her beautiful smile and a head-nod, as he closed the door behind him.

"We only have until just after count time, which is at roughly 4:15 p.m.," She paused, looking at her watch.

"Then you have to go. We only have an hour and fifteen minutes. Where were we?" she asked, crossing her slender arms over her chest.

"I was signing out of my old school," I said dryly.

I was tired. I was looking at the table. She had all these papers scattered around. I noticed the 412 forms that she was talking to Steve about. I wrestled with my thoughts on whether I should ask her if she was going to have to associate me with those 412 forms. I wasn't really feeling that shit.

Fuck it, might as well play this shit out.

All these memories I was reliving were draining my brain. I had to open up a box of feelings I had stored away, and I didn't want to dig up. Hours came and went, and my anxiety about walking out onto the prison yard subsided. I felt a bit relaxed. If she wanted a story, I had a whole book to dish out. I'm going to feed her until she gets full.

"Let's go back. Please tell me how you feel about your father today?" she asked.

She folded her hands together in front of her. This caught me off guard. I wasn't expecting her to ask me a personal question like that.

"What made you ask me a question like that, Ms. Calder?" I said.

She didn't show any emotion like a vet.

"Why do you answer my question with a question? Answer my question first, Mr. Guierra. That is, of course, if you feel comfortable answering it," she smiled devilishly.

She cocked her head to the side, waiting for my answer.

"I'm a man now, Ms. Calder. That shit in the past where I left it. But at the same time, I'll feel more *comfortable...*," I said, using my hands to make air quotations as she did earlier. This got a good laugh from both of us. I continued my sentence.

"...telling the whole story, so I can explain more about my father later."

"OK, you got me there. Can I ask you one more question, then we can move on?" Ms. Calder asked seriously.

"Sure, what is it?"

"Is he still alive? I mean, your father. Is he still living?"

"Yeah, now can we move on?" I asked, getting impatient.

"Please," she said, gesturing with her hand outreached. It was my cue to go on.

CHAPTER TWELVE

I met a few niggas at my new school that were from the different parks in North Miami Beach. Each of them claimed the neighborhood where they lived. I stayed in Greynolds Park. That shit was so square, and there wasn't a chance in hell I would rep that shit.

I stood out for the first couple of months at JFK Middle School, as always. Every time I turned around, they were talking about Megaman and Megaman. I stood alone. I didn't need a crew to be noticed, even though I was missing my old friends.

My friendships with Rah, Fat Boy, and Kirby fizzled within a couple of months of me moving away. Fat Boy was still trying to sell those dreams he had while in boot camp. Fat Boy found himself knee-high in shit when he violated the conditions of his release from boot camp. He got caught with a gun and was facing three years in a Level 10 program. Level 10 was a training prison for juveniles, but for a twelve-year-old, that was a hard time.

He started going around the city fucking with everybody. I wasn't mobile like he was, so I didn't take those trips with him. As a matter of fact, none of us did. He found a connect with some yard weed out in Opa-locka, also known as Choppa-Locka or The Locks, with one of Delroy's cousins. Soon as he got out, he went and bought himself a gun, and that gun landed his ass in jail. I tried to tell him that the money wasn't going anywhere and to be patient, but he insisted. Fat Boy came around one day when Rah brought him to my new house.

"Ain't no money around this motherfucker and shit," Fat Boy said. "I can't vibe like this."

He started tapping his pockets.

"Ain't shit to do. Tell me what we're gonna do then since money wasn't going anywhere?" he asked.

"Shit, if I knew right now, damn my nigga, you won't even give a nigga a chance to think," I said.

"Megaman, my mama out there sucking on that glass dick fool, I'm fucked up, and you talking about shit. I ain't got no time to waste, I know what imma do. Imma take my black ass around these dreads in Opa-locka and get me some money," Fat Boy said.

We both knew there was no saving his drug-addicted mother. Fat Boy was just speeding. He wanted what he wanted, and that got his ass in jail again.

The last time I heard from Rah G was when he came through with Fat Boy. Rah had grown a few inches taller. He had also told me they were trying to put him in a Magnet Program at school. The Magnet Program was an advanced class for the gifted. He ended up throwing it all away to be down. He started smoking and hanging out in Sable Palm Apartments, with some kids we grew up with. He wasn't trying to hear it. He said he was trying to represent Lil Haiti to the fullest.

"I had to smash a few niggas at the schoolhouse, Megaman," Rah said. "You know those chumps tryna try me. They don't respect a nigga mind, so I had to show them niggas what I was thinking."

He got into so much trouble; he was kicked out of all public schools. That was the last time I heard from him.

Kirby still ain't want anything to do with us. After

I moved, I didn't hear from him. Rah told me the two of them almost got into a fight, but he said he would let that nigga be.

Monte was the first nigga I met from Victory Park. I learned all the names of the different parks in the area from the couple niggas I met. There was Uleta Park, Washington Park, Victory Park, and Greynolds Park.

Walking home from school every day, I noticed the same group of kids walking behind me. We would take the same route home until we separated a couple of blocks before mine. They would make all kinds of noise and act stupid all the way from school until I couldn't hear them anymore.

Monte was in my fourth-period class. He was a skinny kid who wore a nappy afro. He noticed me staring at Avia in class one day. I have been crushing on her for a while now. For some reason, she stood out amongst the rest. She wasn't loud or anything. In a way, she made a noise with her beauty. She had these track star legs that were well toned.

Her brown skin looked soft, well moisturized, and flawless. Most times, she wore her natural shoulder-length hair; other times, she wore it in a ponytail. However, she wore it; she looked good. I had a feeling she knew I liked her. Every time we crossed paths, she had her eyes fixed on mine. When she spoke to me, it was the way she said my name that got me. I wasn't sure how I was going to get her, but I had my eyes on her.

"Yo boy, you on little mama really hard, ain't you?" Monte asked, tapping my shoulder.

He sat next to me in class. I didn't think anybody noticed how I was daydreaming and lusting over this girl. I turned to him quickly, startling both of us.

"Huh! What did you say, fool?"

"You staring hard, you might want to cool off before you scare the girl away," Monte laughed.

He was right. It might be a little weird looking and not saying nothing. I noticed that Monte had gold crowns in the center of his bottom teeth.

"I'm tryna bag little mama. What's up with her, though? She got somebody who she fuck with?" I questioned.

"She ain't had a boyfriend yet, but that's just what I heard. I don't know for sure. Don't take my word for it. But this nigga name Bizzy has been with her for a little while now. A lot of these niggas act like she gonna bite because she is pretty. Just get at her, though. All she could do is shoot you down. See that girl over there?" he said.

Monte pointed across the room to a Spanish girl with her head down, doing her classwork.

"That's who I fuck with. That's Jennifer," Monte said.

"She is tight. Lil mama is so quiet, I ain't even notice her," I said.

Monte nodded in agreement.

"I'll get to Avia though, all she's said to a nigga was "Hi Mahkahi", but I got to do more. Imma get at her, though," I said.

"I'm saying, fool, I know you ain't from around here. I could tell by your swag when you first got here. Where did you stay before you moved here?" he asked.

"I just like to do me a fool, I ain't making no noise, but I'm from Lil Haiti," I said confidently.

Lil Haiti brought out the arrogance in kids like me. We loved the hood.

"A lot of niggas from Little Haiti move up this way or North Miami. I stayed in Large Mar Projects before I moved to the V. It's straight-up here though, I like it." Monte' said.

Large Mar was known as LMG, for Large Mar Gangstas. It was north of Little Haiti but wasn't considered Little Haiti.

"Imma go to V after school. You probably don't even know where the V is, huh, because I have never seen you come around there."

"You talking about Victory Park, right?" I asked.

"Yeah, the V," he repeated.

He then explained to me that Victory Park was actually called VP or just V for short.

"I stay on 167th, where the V at?" I asked.

"I see you when you walk home from school. I just ain't know what street you turn on. I am always behind you when you are on your way home," Monte said. I let him continue speaking.

"The V starts on 167th, all the way down to 172nd. After that is Greynolds Park. We'll just be turning on 172nd because my Ace has to check-in and drop his shit at home. Come to Jiffy Store after school, I'll show you where the V is. You know where Jiffy's at, right?" Monte asked.

"Yeah, I know," I answered.

The school was directly behind the 163rd Street Mall. Both the high school and middle school sat adjacent to each other, behind the mall. It seemed like everybody was trying to ditch school. They waited until the high school lunch break to leave, so they could blend in. Kids flooded the streets. From high up in the sky, it probably looked like a bunch of army ants. That's how many people left school at once.

Truancy was a big thing in this area. The police would stop kids from walking the streets during the day. But around lunchtime, the high schoolers could leave for lunch when truancy was harder to detect. It was like having an invisible pass to walk the streets.

I had to walk along the side of the back of the mall, all the way down to Jiffy's on 15th Avenue. It was a straight shot. I saw Jiffy's many times before, driving past. Monte must have skipped with the others because I didn't see him in class in the fourth period. It didn't take much time to get there. As soon as Monte saw me, he started walking in my direction.

"Yo boy, meet my niggas. That's Big D's tall ass."

This dude wore his name in his looks. He was tall and hefty and stood with knocked knees.

"That's Lil V short ass, Ace Boogie, his brother LZ, and last but not least, that's crazy-ass Pouchon. You'll know why they call that nigga that sooner than later."

"Nigga, fuck you," Pouchon said.

He wore a twisted look. He had a dirty red skin tone like he played outside all day. He seemed a little small and skinny for his height. He was skinny but wore the look of a nigga who hugged the block day and night. My intuition never failed me.

After the introductions, we followed Ace to drop his stuff off at his crib. We had to wait for him down the street. Their vibe was different from the other days I saw them after school. It's probably because I was a new face and needed to show them that I was thorough. I knew it was going to take some time, but I was ready for whatever.

The real Victory Park was actually a kid park that sat behind a police station. The police station was attached to the City Hall, and other little departments attached to that building. We had to walk through the police station's sliding doors and down a walkway in the back of all the attached buildings to get to the V. When I looked to my right, a big sign read 'VICTORY PARK' in bold, black letters. On my left was a playground with two swings, a slide, monkey bars, and shredded tires all over the ground. The shredded tires were there as cushions, so the kids wouldn't hurt themselves while playing. I wonder what made them name their hood after a park for little kids.

When we stepped past the park onto the sidewalk, I saw why. Niggas were on bikes riding up and down the block like they owned it. Other niggas were serving fiends out of sight behind buildings. These niggas were hustling hard. The way they looked and the way they dressed was a dead giveaway. Most of what I saw was what I knew from experience. The average motherfucker would have missed the whole lick. These niggas were brave.

"This is the V," Monte said.

He breathed in and spread his arms in a grandiose gesture. I now understood the meaning behind Victory. This was their trademark. They owned these streets. I wanted to be down with these niggas, and I hadn't seen half of them yet.

As we walked across the street, I took in the scenery. There was a full basketball court to the right, with a game going on. A large crowd formed around the game. It was mostly females cheering for who they came to see.

We walked into the famous 2020 building across the street. You wouldn't expect to walk into the shit that was going on inside. When you got inside, you wished you'd never gone in. The fact that this was a crime watch area, I wondered how these niggas got away with doing all this. A junkie stood next to the elevator on my left, checking what he bought from a nigga. I saw him looking over his shoulder at us, trying to hide it. He had better be glad it was us and not the cops because he would have been caught. There are three ways to go once you're past the main entrance: left, right, or straight ahead to the elevator.

"Nigga, I got a hundred dollar stop on that Zoe," Tiki yelled, who I later found out was Monte's older brother.

"Double that nigga, I got two hundred in the bank. That little hundred ain't making no noise, fool," another guy holding the dice yelled.

He shook the dice in his fist. They were playing *C-low* by the corner stairs, down the left side of the hallway.

"Bet nigga! That hoe sweet nigga," the guy said, referring to the dice.

As I got closer, I saw Tiki throw the dice in an awkward stance squatting down. Even when he let go of the dice, he was still shaking his hands as the dice rolled in the direction of the other guy. The guy stomped his feet toward the dice as if to taunt them, biting his lower lip.

"That's my money nigga, the dice hit your feet. Yo, money burnt. Let me get that playa," Tiki said seriously.

Tiki explained that the dice couldn't touch anything around them until they stopped rolling on the floor. He made it clear that he explained that rule before they started playing, and he had the bank.

"You got me fucked up nigga. Dice go over. I ain't heard you say that shit," the guy yelled back.

"Nah nigga, you got me fucked up," Tiki responded.

Tiki reached under his shirt. I never got to see what happened next because Monte' ushered me past the argument, and he pulled me from the crowd. Monte said they always go through it about a dice game. He explained the rules of the game and promised to show me how to play one day.

Monte showed me the whole of Victory Park in an hour. It stretched out five blocks up, and three blocks down. There were four main buildings: 2020, 2150, Manchester, and Kings Place. 2020 sat on 20th Avenue and was one of the two buildings run by the VP boys. 2150 sat on 21st

Avenue and was run by T.A.Z. or Tough Ass Zoes. It was crazy to me how shit worked in between these buildings.

"Imma tell you how this shit is. See them niggas down there? In 2150? They don't go past that building right there," he said, pointing at a duplex that was in the middle of the block.

"2020 niggas got seniority because they sort of like OG's, but they respect the T.A.Z. Dudes because they are young, and they are tryna get some money. Nobody goes to the Manchester and King buildings unless it gets hot, but you'll see how that shit works, just keep coming around here. And don't be acting like you friendly and shit because a nigga might try you." he laughed.

"I got this fool, let me do my part, you do yours," I replied.

I wanted to make sure he understood I was not lame.

"This ain't Lil Haiti, Megaman, and these niggas ain't pussies. Most of these niggas come from where you come from. But around here, niggas ain't trying to go through all that. They are trying to get paper, feel me?" Monte' said.

He further explained other areas around the V. He told me where I should stay away from, which was the cracker's neighborhood. I figured it out. I had to get in where I fit in. I was about that paper too, but it was getting in with these dudes that made me worried. They were a different breed.

I hadn't been here long enough to know the ins and outs, and I needed to analyze things. My options were still open. For the next two hours, I hung out with the niggas I had just met. We went back across the street by the basketball court. As time went by, the whole area started to look like a block party. The benches along the courts and sidewalks were crammed with people. I stood there in silence, overlooking the scene in awe.

CHAPTER THIRTEEN

In just a few months, the V became my stomping grounds. I was there every day and night. I became known as the kid with all the go-karts and dirt bikes. We would go to Highland Oaks, the predominated white neighborhood that Monte' told me to stay away from and steal our asses off. They were always leaving shit out. If you went back to the same house the next day, they would leave something else out there for you to take. To me, they were just naïve. I thought all people with money were. So, every time they left it out, we took it.

My mom worked a late-night shift. She worked all night, and a couple of hours during the day if they needed her. She ended up going back to school to get her nursing certificate. Her persistence paid off. After receiving her certificate, she was paid more, and it seemed like our family moved up. Living in North Miami Beach was expensive. If she wanted to keep up with the bills, she had no choice but to get a better job.

The good part about staying in North Miami Beach was they had Crime Watch. It might not have worked for all the thievery going on, but I didn't have to be scared to step outside. I wasn't worried whether someone might knock my head off with the chopper. I left the house every chance I got without a worry in the world. I would go out the back door when she was leaving out the front. I always took the same route to the V; through the back alley, all the way down 18th Avenue, and crossed the main street into Victory

Park. Some days I wouldl find myself rushing back to meet my mom at home.

My neighborhood, Greynolds Park, was boring as hell. The little white boy Jason came by my house all the time, wanting me to play with him. When I finally played with him, that shit wasn't about nothing. He was a square, and I felt like I had to dumb myself down to talk to him. He ain't understand no slang, so it was weird trying to stay on his level. He acted like he wasn't attracted to girls. This girl named Amy stayed right down the street from us. She made it her business to let us know she liked this boy. He ran from her every time it was time for them to make out. He said his parents said it was inappropriate at that age to kiss. Fuck that. I couldn't be around him anymore.

In the V, shit was going down. If you got a girl to like you, you were at least touching some pussy. You might get none, but you got to touch or see it. I was working on trying to get me some. One day when my mother left for work, I went out the back door, got on my bike, and took the same route I always took to the V.

As soon as I got to the park, I saw Ace posted up outside the kiddie park kicking it with a broad. I asked him where everybody else was. He told me they were at the monkey bars with some other broads. I was just in time to catch Big D roll a blunt the size of a cigar. When he was done, I was only able to hit it a few times. I still had fresh lungs, and the D roll hit me hard. All of a sudden, someone grabbed me by my collar from the back.

Before I could turn around, a pair of hands were beating on my back. The hands came down so fast, I didn't have time to react. My ears were ringing from where the blows landed. The person didn't say a word, just kept hitting me. It was slightly weak, but it scared the shit out of me. I finally caught a glimpse of my mom's hospital, scrubs. Her small hands were swinging wildly. I turned around quickly.

"Ma, chill," I pleaded.

When everyone realized who she was, they took off running. When my mama got mad, it seemed like she released all the pent-up anger and stress from the last couple of years.

"Tout. Bagay. Mwen. Fe. Pou. Ou." she yelled in creole.

She continued to whoop my ass. When she was done embarrassing me, she didn't have to tell me to get in the car. She parked around where the basketball court was. When we pulled up in front of the house, she didn't have to tell me I couldn't leave the house.

I don't know who told my mom that I was leaving the house. I thought I made sure I covered my tracks. I would put Disha to sleep and come back to check on her every so often. I couldn't figure out who told her.

That same week, this girl came walking into my house named Angelica. She and my mother sat in the living room and talked for an hour or so. I was trying to ear hustle, but I couldn't hear exactly what was being said. Angelica was pretty. She had this mocha skin like an Indian, but she spoke fluent French and English. Her hair was in locks thrown to one side over her shoulder. I went into the kitchen, pretending I wanted something to drink. She waved at me as I passed by. I waved back and watched as she stood up first and shook my mom's hand. My mom was about 5'3,", and Angelica was a little shorter than my mom. We were probably around the same height. She had this high school swag about her, or maybe she was in college. She had all these books in her hands like she just left the library. It made her look like she was sophisticated. That same night, she was at my house dressed in shorts and a tank top with Mickey

Mouse on the front. She carried a book bag that looked like it was full of shit. *Who the fuck is she, and why do I feel like they got me guessing on purpose?*

Before my mother left, she gave me the 'eye' and signaled Angelica to follow her into the kitchen. I followed close behind them. She was showing her some phone numbers she wrote on a little board in the kitchen. She explained to Angelica that the extensions next to the numbers were to the hospital where she worked just in case she called. She wanted her to have direct access to find her.

When my mom left that night, Angelica ran down the basics. She explained that she was the babysitter now that my mom worked late nights. She told me she would be sleeping over. She made it clear that she had to keep an eye on me since I liked to sneak out. I wasn't trying to hear that shit. I was going to sneak out regardless. Angelica said she went to North Miami Beach High School. Every morning my mom would drop her off when she dropped Disha and me at school. Disha's school was up the street, and my Junior High was next door to NMB.

Angelica had been at my house every weekend for a month. One night I was getting out of the shower, getting ready for bed, and this broad Angelica was at the bathroom door watching me dry off. When I saw her, it scared the shit out of me so badly, I slipped in the tub trying to cover up. She helped me up, but the way she touched me made my dick get hard. Her eyes were fixed on my genitals. I forgot I was naked. The pain in my head from the fall distracted me. She handed me my towel with a smile, never looking into my eyes. I had a feeling someone had been watching me; now, I knew who it was.

I had developed over the years, and my body had shaped up nicely. The only active thing I did was run from the police and play pick-up football every now and then. My mom couldn't afford for me to play Pop Warner Football. I had too much street in me to be worried about anything else anyway.

My abs started coming in, and my chest started to spread. Puberty had taken its course. Over the last couple of weeks, I thought I was coming down with a cold. After my throat finally cleared up, I found my voice had deepened. People would say I still looked young and that I was the spitting image of Muhammad Ali. My eyes complimented my cinnamon-brown skin. I had waves spinning all around my head in a circle. Monte showed me how to brush them, keep them shiny, and lay them down with a Du-Rag at night before I went to sleep.

As I sat on the couch, I overheard Angelica talking on the phone. She made it no secret that she had a thing for me.

"Girl, he is so cute. He got these light brown eyes and these deep-ass waves all over his sexy head. I don't give a fuck if he is a young bitch, you need to see what the nigga is working with. Girl, you just don't know," she said.

Angelica looked me straight in the face smiling. I acted like I ain't know she was talking about me.

I stopped sneaking out because I was enjoying Angelica's company. Why sneak out if I had a girl at home? She let me do me. We would take turns with the remote trying to find things to watch, but this particular night would be a night to remember.

"What are you tryna watch, Mahkahi? I can't find nothing on TV," she said.

The way she looked at me when she questioned me did things to my body. It was like my opinion meant something to her.

"I don't care," I said.

I laid on the ground on my stomach in front of the TV with a bowl of Combos pretzels on one side and soda on the other.

She got up and went into her bag. I watched her out the side of my eye. She walked over to Disha's room. When she came out of Disha's room, she pulled the door closed behind her. She walked over to the front door to make sure it was locked and made sure the blinds were closed. I watched her in silence.

She had on this sexy-ass sundress that hugged her body flawlessly. Her bare feet weren't done, but I noticed a tattoo of a flower on her foot. When she was done, she walked over to the DVD player and held a DVD up for me to see.

"Look, if I put this movie on, you promise not to tell yo mama, right?" she asked seriously.

"Angelica, I might be young, but I ain't no lame. You and I know I ain't telling on shit."

"Don't get all shy and shit when you see this," she said.

She put the DVD in the player. Her attitude was gritty now that she was getting comfortable with me. That good girl act she put on for my mom was out the door when my mom left for work.

When she stuck the DVD in, the first scene was a dark-skinned woman bent over, holding her ass apart. Another woman was squatting on the side of her with her tongue out, pretending to lick her butt. The options screen popped up, and Angelica scrolled to the language, picked English, then went back up and hit Play. She walked back to her spot. While all this was going on, she was standing over me, giving me a panty shot under her sundress. She could have used the remote, but she had other plans.

The screen changed to a woman lying on the bed

wearing glasses and reading a book. Her hair sat on top of her head in a windmill-type hairdo. The only people I know who can pull that hairstyle off were people with long hair. She looked sophisticated. A black man walked into the room wearing some tight-ass pants, no shirt, a construction hat, and a tool belt. He walked right up to the woman, and they stared at each other for a moment, then kissed each other passionately. The next thing I knew, he was sucking the hell out of her pussy. It oozed creamy shit. I'm thinking to myself, *"how he put that nasty shit in his mouth?"*

I still got excited, but I was trying not to overreact. I wanted to know what Angelica was thinking. My blood was pumping in one direction. I have never had sex before, but right now, Angelica could get it. I was scared to get off my stomach for fear of my dick busting out my pants.

"Don't tell me you never watched a flick before," she said behind me.

I turned around slowly and shook my head, yeah. I've seen plenty of flicks, but why were we watching one and not acting it out, I wanted to say. Angelica stood up like she was going to change the DVD. The expression on her face was slick. When she laid next to me, I could feel the heat coming from her body. My intuition told me she wanted to fuck. I kept my eyes glued to the TV like she wasn't there. I watched as the woman lay on her back with her knees all the way to her shoulders, taking all of him in her, her pussy still oozing creamy shit.

I was getting harder by the second watching all the theatrics going on. I wanted to get up and fix myself, but I wanted to show Angelica this was nothing to me. I wanted to show I had control, even though I didn't.

Without warning, Angelica pulled me over to her, making me lay right under her, my back on the floor. *Is this real?*

Then she laid on top of me. She kissed me hungrily all over my mouth, leaving my lips wet on the top and bottom, turning me off. I kept glancing back at the screen for momentum. While she kissed me, the bottom half of her body moved in a circular motion. At first, it felt awkward until I caught her rhythm. There was so much friction between us that I had to find a way to get some space before I busted a nut. If I didn't stop her, I was definitely going to.

"Hold up, I can't breathe, Angelica," I said, stopping her.

She had her eyes closed at the moment. When she let up, we took things a little slower. I had to show her how to kiss.

"Just follow me, slowly," I instructed.

I put my lips to hers and began doing what I knew, and she followed suit. It was one of those each-one-teach-one moments. We kissed for a while until we got tired.

"OK, take off your clothes now!" she demanded.

I hesitated, then took my shirt off first. She helped me pull off my pants and left me in nothing but my boxers. When I looked down, my excitement was evident. She stood over me, pulling her dress over the top of her head. The bra and panties she wore had hearts all over them. Her pussy was really bushy. I couldn't see her lips or her clit. When she took off her bra, her breasts were a mouth full. She was a slim girl, which was something I liked about her. She didn't have full breasts like Black Barbie. She looked innocent, almost like a virgin, like she's never been tampered with. But of course, I knew better.

"Suck on my nipples," she sat on top of me.

I sat up, not knowing what to do.

"Not so hard! Damn boy, calm down, just lick and suck around the nipple real soft like you kiss," she instructed.

I did what I was told.

Then I heard the moaning start. My ego shot up to the roof. We were sitting up, and she slowly slid down, backward, until she was on top of me, and her lips were on mine. She teased my body for a little while, kissing me on my chest, then up my neck. I could tell she wasn't experienced, but that she had done this before. I tried a move I saw Scoot demonstrate on Barbie. I massaged the back of her neck, and it caused her to kiss harder. I flipped her on her back and did the same thing she did to me but added the ear licking trick that Scoot taught me. That sent the bottom half of her body up to me. She reached up and down and found the gap in my boxers, and her hands found their way to my genitals. I couldn't believe how stiff I was. It was so hard, I started getting nauseous.

"Put it in," she moaned, kissing me feverishly.

I impatiently pulled my dick out. I tried a couple of times but couldn't find the hole. My fingers were drenched from her wetness. She stained the floor, leaving wet spots on the carpet with every move she made. When I tried to push it in, I kept hitting a wall. She refused to help at first. Instead, she was bracing her body for my entrance. I finally gave up.

"I don't know how," I said honestly. "I have never done this before. You put it in."

She took my hand and guided it past her bush into her opening. She was running like a busted pipe. I felt around her lips, it was sticky and soft. Every time I stuck my finger at her entrance, she moaned and moved forward.

"Put it in," she moaned again.

I traced my fingers back in the same direction I went in, making a mental map. I grabbed myself and guided the tip.

"Not so rough, boy," she whispered.

She started moving away from me.

"Rub it at the tip first, then go in slowly," she whispered.

Her body shivered with anticipation. Her insides felt warm and inviting. I did as I was told, going in and out of her very slowly. I went in maybe four or five times at the most before feeling my body going limp. I picked up the pace and ended up losing control. I felt my blood rush to my dick before sending my juices deep inside her. I collapsed on her shoulder, drooling. She pushed me off her immediately.

"You can't cum inside of me, why you ain't tell me you were cumming? Damn!" she yelled.

She looked down at me.

"I could get pregnant like that. I see I have a lot to teach you. When you finish with me, you'll have some fire dick. That was good, Mahkahi. You might be working with something," she said, smiling at me.

For the rest of the night, we lusted over each other. We continued to have sex over and over, each time trying to go a little longer. From seconds to minutes, to a full five minutes. I made that five-minute count too. She told me I couldn't try to beat her pussy up every time we fucked. I had to finesse it. Every night after that, it was the same routine. Then she started bringing condoms with her. I took this show on the road, fucking girls at school, and all over the neighborhood. Half the boys around my age weren't having sex yet until they started hanging around me. There was one girl I had yet to touch, but I was determined to.

CHAPTER FOURTEEN

We weren't living in North Miami Beach for a year when my mom met this El Debarge looking dude named Simon. He was an African American man who spoke Creole as a second language. She fell in love quickly, and this was the first time I had seen her happy since the incident with my father. Simon was a fair guy. He worked hard and had his own shit before he met my mom. I felt as long as mama was happy, I was happy.

I was in the living room, kicked back, watching TV, when my mom came and sat next to me. She bought Disha and me our own television sets for our rooms. Between school and running the streets all day, I was too tired to go any farther than the living room.

"You are mighty comfortable. Why are you not in your room doing homework? The first thing you did when you came in turned the TV on." She said.

She kept going on about school stuff, then kicked off her shoes and got comfortable next to me. She started to rub my little curly afro. I started growing it four months ago. I thought about getting some braids, but I had to see if she was going on a trip about the afro first.

"You need a haircut. Imma leave you some money so you can cut that stuff off," she said.

Every time she gave me money, I did something else with it. I thought she would just catch on and stop bringing it up.

"Grandma Nah-Nah is sick, Kahi. She's coming to stay with us for a while."

"What happened to Grandma Nah-Nah? When we went to see her at Auntie Ket-Ket house, she looked alright to me," I said.

"Looks can be deceiving son. You can't always judge a book by its cover. Your grandma always cooks all that greasy stuff, and the doctors had already warned her about eating like that. She had a stroke earlier today, and I had to leave work early to be at the hospital with her all day," she said.

As she talked, her lips quivered while she fought back the tears. She was still running her fingers through my hair. I didn't know what a stroke was, and I didn't ask. I could tell it was serious from my mom's facial expressions. Grandma Nah-Nah was good in the kitchen. She was a perfectionist, and it demanded her to fall in love with the process of making food. I tried to wrestle with her being sick, but I couldn't remember her acting any differently.

Disha had inherited Grandma Nah-Nah's cat-like eyes, her pupils looking like little slits. She had yellow and brown streaks going around them. They were beautiful. She was a light-skinned woman; some people would have mistaken her for a white woman. Rah G saw her visit one time in Little Haiti and thought that she was a social worker. I loved my Grandma. Hell, she was the only Grandma I knew. My father's side of the family was distant. I thought I heard my mom and Auntie Ket-Ket, arguing about who was going to take care of my Grandma. Auntie Ket-Ket was well off since she came to the states. She and her husband had great jobs, and only one child to support. Auntie Ket-Ket was a woman who selfishly loved her privacy. She was trying to build her own family, and that's all the responsibility she wanted.

Simon had just moved into our three-bedroom house. With the four of us, there was just enough space. Grandma moving in and being sick was going to make it a tight spot.

"Next week or so, when I come home from work, we need to sit down and figure out how we're going to help Grandma Nah-Nah as a family. As if the bills aren't already enough," she said.

"She shook her head. I haven't paid Angelica in two weeks. The poor girl said it was OK. I still feel bad. I need to figure this out."

Tears rolled down her face.

"Don't cry, ma. Don't worry about Angelica. She ain't worried about no money, she just likes being here," I said.

"What makes you say that? Angelica tells you things like that?" she questioned.

She looked at me sideways.

"Chill old lady, I got this," I smiled.

I told her everything was going to be alright. I wasn't trying to get rid of Angelica. Truthfully, my mom knew damn well I didn't need a babysitter in the first place. She hired Angelica out of spite to try and tame me. I was growing up, and she had to face it.

Angelica knew that my mother had a lot of shit on her plate, and as far as I was concerned, little mama was doing a great job. There was no way I wanted her to go anywhere. She introduced me to the world of sex and had been a good teacher. For the first time since we been having sex, Angelica gave me some head. She told me sometimes she would do that to keep me happy and satisfied. She said I liked to beat her pussy up, and it needed a break from time to time. I didn't complain at all. After a while, I was a regular at her drive through, and she knew exactly what I wanted.

"You're getting older, Kahi," my mother said.

"You always had a good heart, I just wished you'd stop getting in all that trouble. If something happens to me, who do you think is gonna have to step up? Do you hear me talking to you, Mahkahi?" she asked.

She turned my head so she could look me in my face.

"If something happens to me, baby, nobody is going to step up for you, son. It's just you. Kadisha is your sister, and I'm your mother. The women in your family are queens, Mahkahi. When I'm gone, it doesn't stop with me, OK?"

As she spoke, tears fell freely from her eyes.

"Stop talking like something is gonna happen to you, ma. I promise when I get older and get some real money, Imma buy you whatever you want, but in life, you never know what curve balls will get thrown at you."

For some reason, at that very age, I understood that.

She started to cry, letting me go. I cuffed her face in her hands. I pulled her to me this time. The pain in her eyes said a lot. There wasn't a hint of happy tears, and it broke my heart. She let it all go, let me console her. I started to cry because she made me feel what she felt. We held on to each other like this was going to be the last time we would ever get to hold each other like this again.

A couple of weeks later, when she came from work, we had a meeting, and she dropped the bombshell on us. Today was Simon's day off, and we were expecting Grandma to be dropped off. All of Grandma's things were already in Disha's room. Disha didn't mind because she was a welcoming child. My sister enjoyed the company from anyone in the family. We all sat in the living room, my mother still in her scrubs. Her face was red, and her eyes puffy. She looked like she did the last time we cried together. She had been crying again. I couldn't understand why she was so emotional. Damn, is it that bad? I thought to myself. This woman was usually either extra angry or extra happy but sadness wasn't in her DNA.

"Mahkahi, Kadisha," she said. "I have something to tell you all. Are you all listening? You are all about to have a baby sister. Simon and I are having a baby."

Simon's arm was around her shoulder for support. I was both happy and a little disappointed. I didn't need anybody else added to this family. A baby meant more bills, and Grandma was already moving in. The fact that we were about to have all these people in this house meant my whole world was about to change again. If she was having a baby with this man, I wondered what my father was thinking. Then again, he might not even know. I thought she was still loyal to him and wouldn't do something like this. I was young and still trying to understand. I became distant. The next few seconds, minutes, days, and months flew by, and unwanted circumstances knocked at the front door.

CHAPTER FIFTEEN

Halfway into my mom's pregnancy, the burden of having Grandma Nah-Nah living with us, the new baby coming, and me getting in trouble at school and the streets, drove my mother up the wall. After seeing my Grandma had a stroke, I knew that was something I never wanted to deal with. The whole left side of her body was paralyzed. Her left arm hung loosely from her body, while her leg dragged when she walked, making her look like a zombie. She had a walker that made loud screeching noises on the floor when she moved around the house. It was terrible. The simple things people were able to do every day were difficult for my Nah-Nah.

Grandma Nah-Nah was a strong black woman who prided herself on self-taught skills like cooking, which was her specialty. Now she was reduced, and her pride wounded. It reminded me of my father when he was put in a wheelchair. We tried our best to keep it together, but our in-house feuds got the best of us. I broke promises that I made to my mother, and she reminded me every time she went on one of her rants.

Being in the streets more, I ended up going to jail, fucking with LZ's crazy-ass. We were caught trying to steal a car. We didn't even get a chance to take it for a drive. LZ showed me a trick to use with any car key. We would shave the key until it was smooth, and the teeth were almost sharp as a knife. We used that key to get the car started by shaking the steering column and turning the key at the same time. The car would crank right up. Sometimes it took both of us to get the job done. I fucked up one day when it was my turn to watch out.

I put my head down, staring at a spider eating a moth against tree bark. By the time I looked up, a police officer was easing up while LZ was trying to break the key in. The trouble didn't stop there.

As time went on, I spent more time with my friends than with my family. I was getting tired of my mother's mood swings, and I started to hate the fact that she was pregnant. Eventually, my troubles got the best of me. Soon I got kicked out of public school temporarily. It started when I brought some girls around to keep us company on the way home. Her name was Danielle Waters. I met one of the girls in history class. She had a bunch of sisters, two went to our school, and three went to high school. Only three of them were her mother's children, but they loved each other the same. Danielle was a sporty chick, a bar of polished chocolate treats. She was the prettiest black I ever saw. Whatever she wanted, she got: big hoop earrings, the latest shoes, boy and girl chain-sets. You name it; she had it. She told me she lost her mother when she was in the fourth grade. Danielle said her father was always doing business and that he had money. This is why he spoiled her and her sisters so much. She was the baby and the most spoiled out of the girls. Her sassiness came from her ghetto-ass sister Monkey Red, that was a year older than Danielle. They were like day and night. Monkey Red was light-skinned and wild, while Danielle was dark-skinned and less crazy than her sister. I liked Danielle a lot, but I still wanted Avia for a girlfriend. The only problem was Avia wasn't thinking about being my girlfriend. It was still a work in progress.

While we were walking home from school, we talked about going to the city pool in Victory Park the next day.

"What's up? You all tryna go to the pool tomorrow or what?" Ace asked.

I was surprised because he barely spoke when we were in a group of people. He wasn't shy, he just usually went with the flow.

"Hell yeah," Monkey Red spoke up first. "Man, I'm telling you a bitch could do all kinds of shit in that mother-fucking pool: backstroke, slow stroke, whatever."

Everybody busted out laughing. She was funny and wild with everything she did. We all agreed to meet in front of the pool until everybody showed up. Danielle showed up with ten of her friends. Some were from the previous day, and some I didn't know. They were all looking good. Danielle wore a crop top shirt, showing off her belly button. She had on short-shorts and some see-through jelly shoes. Her whole outfit was purple and pink. She even took the time out to paint her nails the same color. I liked what I saw.

"That's that nigga Jux-Box from U.P.," Big D said.

He slid next to me. They walked ahead of us going in the same direction.

Jux-Box was a pretty-ass nigga who was with a gang around the school who called themselves P.B.G., short for Pretty Boy Gangstas. He was now with these niggas from U.P. I saw him in action. He was pretty nice with his hands. I wasn't fazed by their presence. I shook my head and watched him, and his people went into the gate.

"I don't like that nigga. Fool think a nigga won't whoop his ass," Big D said through clenched teeth.

Those U.P. boys were just another headache the V had to deal with. The beef between them went back to middle school.

"Hey, ya'll ready, fellas?" Danielle said.

She snapped her fingers in the air, getting our attention. Ace, LZ, and Monte led the pack towards the pool, followed by the females, with me, and Big D in the back.

"Check this out fool. We got these hiz-hoes. I don't know what you're gonna do, but imma tries to get my feel on. You in or you out?" I asked, motioning with the bottom half of my body. The big man smiled and followed suit.

We paid our fee at the entrance and went in. The guys and the girls split into two groups, each of us going into our respective locker rooms to change. Monte and I headed to the diving boards, already dressed for the occasion. Swimming came naturally to me. I can't remember a time when I had to learn. At night, Monte, LZ, and I would jump the gate to practice our dives on the diving boards. All the practice I had been doing was for this day. Not even five minutes later, LZ came running around the corner to rain on my parade.

"Yo boy, check this out, fool," LZ said.

He rushed up to the board. I was up next, and one of the lifeguards was screaming for him to get in line.

"Hold up, kid! I'm next up," I said.

I looked back, hoping the lifeguard didn't come to throw both of us out of line. At first glance, I didn't notice the commotion beyond the lifeguard tower. I squinted my eyes, and the commotion was obvious. Looking into LZ's eyes, I knew this was serious.

"Nah, fuck that. Flex and Big D are about to fight," LZ said, looking in the direction of the commotion. "I don't like where the rest of them niggas are," he said.

LZ spoke rapidly, losing his breath. Flex was one of Jux-Box's flunkies who I noticed followed Jux-Box around like a puppy. I whistled towards Monte, who was a few feet away from me, vibing with one of Danielle's friends. We made the call of whistling our thing in case we broke up one day on one of our capers.

By the time we got to Big D, his back was against a wall outside of the men's locker room. He was throwing rapid punches at Flex and another kid who was trying to jump in. Big D looked like a bear backed in a corner by two starving wolves. When we got closer, LZ lunged at the other kid, knocking him down from the blindside.

I reacted by trying to stomp the kid out. Unbeknownst to me, three guys were lying in wait. I ran around to hit Flex, who, in turn, got his lick back when he and his goons surrounded me. I was outnumbered and praying for a way out.

Looking around for an exit, I saw Ace standing toe to toe with Jux-Box. It was like watching Mike Tyson fight himself. I was told Ace had some mean hands, and Jux-Box apparently did too.

I was too small to stand up and fight three people at one time. Luckily for me, that's when a whistle was blown. A lifeguard showed up with the police. I have never been so happy to see the police in my life. We ended up with a warning from the police and were banned from the pool for the rest of the summer.

On our walk home, everyone was drilling Monte about where he was when shit popped off. I knew he heard the call because he looked right at me, throwing his hands up like I was fucking up a good thing between him and his possible. Throughout all that chaos, he showed up when the show was over. Monte said he stalled a bit because he ain't think it was that serious. He got some real backlash behind that move, and the other fellas felt some type of way.

Two weeks later, Jux-Box and I crossed paths in the hallway at school and exchanged some words. My pride wouldn't allow me to let him call me a fuck-boy in front of people the way he did. He had fucked up. He must have thought I was a pussy or something. He sent his number one flunky, Flex at me like I was going to back down. Little did he know I was about that life, and this was the biggest mistake of the year.

I was born for this type of hit. Anybody in my weight class who thought I was a pushover; I was crushing them. I saw it coming. Flex walked up on me too aggressively, with his fist balled up. After that fight with Pale, Scoot taught me to always hide my intentions and never let my left hand know what my right hand is doing.

I fell back a few feet, standing calm as if I didn't expect a thing. I watched my opponent. I let him think he had an advantage, but in reality, I was giving myself space in case they wanted to do to me what they tried to do to Big D. I was outnumbered, but I had to prove to Jux-Box that I wasn't a fuck-boy, but a real nigga. I was running with the V, and to let them down meant I let myself down.

"What the fuck are you looking at, pussy-ass nigga?" Flex boomed, swinging a wild left.

I anticipated the right, so I put my left leg forward and right leg back. I thought he was a righty. He tried to trick me, but my reflexes beat his slow-ass blow. I ducked and came up with a short right, followed by a kick to his leg, then a left that knocked him back. The kick wasn't hard, it was just a distraction. Growing up in Little Haiti, you had to fight to survive. I learned not to let up unless your opponent gave up, or someone stopped the fight. I kept swinging, connecting with every blow. LZ came out of nowhere, scaring me, and causing me to jump back. I prepared to launch another blow. He never looked at me, his eyes were on the target, his feet driving right into Flex's midsection.

Jux-Box started to run in our direction, only to stop when he heard the security yelling. I thought to myself that we were saved by the authorities again.

Like a flash, LZ was in the wind with the crowd. I got cornered by two security guards. They pinned me to the wall with an elbow to the back of the neck. Flex laid on the floor, clutching at his side in pain. We made eye contact, and I winked at him. He looked up at the ceiling defeated, while the school nurse and another person helped him onto a stretcher. The whole school showed up. I knew I had won this round.

Who's the pussy now?

Unfortunately, I was the only person charged with his attack. I wouldn't name anybody else. The school principal refused to believe that the cracked rib and large gash above Flex's eye were done by one person.

"It ain't my fault I hit hard," I said, showing the principal a balled-up fist.

That cracker looked at me like I had gone mad before kicking me out of his school and sending me to Opportunity School. The Opportunity School was way out west, called Jann Mann. Boy, did that piss my mama off! The first person I ran into when I started, was Lil V from Victory Park. He told me that he had been there since the first quarter of seventh grade. He didn't go intowhy he got sent there.

"All kinds of shit," was his own explanation.

"You should have seen how we whooped the nigga Flex who Jux-Box was with. LZ came through, and we beat that nigga ass, cracked his ribs, and some more shit," I bragged.

I told Lil V about the whole situation. I went into details

about how it happened, how it all started at the pool, and how I ended up coming to Jann Mann. Lil V was more upset about missing the action than he was about what happened.

"Damn my nigga, they tried to jump Big D. We gotta talk to that nigga Monte for slipping on us like that. V.P. and U.P. have been beefing, and Monte knows this. It's good you whooped that nigga Flex's ass. Jux-Box is gonna have to get him, though. That's on V, my nigga. He always starts shit," Lil V said, mean-mugging.

He was obviously frustrated. Shit, I was too. Jux-Box slipped through the cracks, and he wasn't putting in no work.

"'Fuck all that though. How is school? It feels like there is a whole lot of tension in the air," I said.

I looked around at all the hard faces around me.

"It's cool. This is a whole different vibe though; you know them Yanks and Haitians beefing. You know how that shit is," he said. "Black Americans and Haitians have been at war since back in the days. I'll tell you about it later. Pouchon crazy-ass went out here too, but he got locked up again," Lil V said.

"Damn, every time you blink, this nigga Pouchon jammed-up. What for now?" I asked.

It was true; most of the time, Pouchon was either in jail or cooking up a recipe to go to jail.

"Pouchon fuckin around the Jiffy Store with that square-ass nigga, Bar. That nigga dropped the boom right next to Pouchon feet when nine rolled up, and Bar ain't tell them shit." Lil V said, shaking his head.

"That's fucked up. That nigga would've had to see me right in front of the police. I would've beaten his ass. That's some creepy-ass shit," I said.

I wondered to myself what Pouchon was doing hanging with this creep, crumb snatching-ass nigga anyways.

Finally, I got ready to walk away.

"Let me go find out who class I'm in," I said.

Lil V grabbed my arm, pulling me close enough so I would be the only person to hear him. People walked by us hurriedly, but I noticed the hard stares from others.

"Don't get friendly with all these niggas. Them Yanks don't really fuck with us," he said seriously, walking away.

CHAPTER SIXTEEN

"**W**hich way you tryna go because KP said the bath-room window is always open and the dude doesn't lock the sliding door," LZ said to Monte.

We were on the way to commit a B&E or breaking and entering; our new hustle. An older head from the V named KP put LZ on the lick. He told a nigga name Pico; time was up. He said the nigga house we were breaking into owed him some change. He didn't say what, but he was going to teach him a lesson. There was supposed to be some dope and guns in the house, and he said we could keep half of anything we took. He knew exactly where this nigga Pico kept his shit since Pico and KP were friends at one time. Now we know trust is a blind man's game.

"Let's go through the window because you remember what happened the last time, we tried the sliding door, Megaman," Monte said.

He was referring to a time we were on our way to school. Monte was scoping this house that was always vacant. Whoever lived there was never home. The only time Monte said he saw a car in the driveway was on the way home. When we tried breaking in through the sliding door, we set off an alarm that sounded like a fire truck setting off its siren. We were lucky to get away, but after that, we learned that most people never put an alarm on their bathroom windows.

LZ was the first through the window, then Monte, and then me. I used a mini crowbar to slide the window open with ease. The outside of the house was poorly maintained. The paint had been chipping on the side of the house where the bathroom window was. The grass was unkempt and needed some grooming.

One look at this house from the outside and you would have thought no one lived there. On the inside, it was a different story. Designer red tile covered the entire bathroom floor, the hand towels were green and red Gucci. Pico was a big spender, and from the looks of his bathroom, he spent in style.

Before I went out the door, I noticed a television that sat in front of the toilet, mounted on a wall, so that when taking a shit, you could watch TV. That shit tripped me out. We chose the master bathroom window. There, we saw jewelry sprawled out on the dresser. There was a hand-painted portrait of a man in all white, with a king's crown on his head, placed directly above the master's bed. I saw Pico before, and that was definitely him. He had these eyes that told a hustler's story, but it was hard to hold his gaze. He always had this look like he was analyzing. I felt like the painting was staring directly at me.

"Megaman, you know the routine. We got to check the whole house first. Make sure nobody is in this mother-fucker" Monte whispered, breaking me out of my thoughts.

We crept through the hallway seeing more art along the walls. There were paintings by Scarface the rapper, Tupac, Biggie, Scarface the drug dealer, and a cartoon painting by Pico. He had a big head, with a Chicago Bulls' jersey set on, reenacting Jordan's winning shot in the final seconds of the game against the Lakers.

After we checked all four rooms, we cleared the living room together, going straight for the guns. There was a sawed-off shotgun trapped between the cabinets and the refrigerator. Monte stepped on the kitchen counter and reached inside the cupboard where a 9mm was taped in the back. LZ walked over to the couch. Starting from the front door, he walked to the third seat, reached under the seat, and came up with another 9mm.

"Imma go get the yay, you all can go to the rooms and grab whatever we can sell, so we can make a little extra change. Meet me in the hallway in five minutes. Then we went out, so we hurry up!" Monte said.

We scrambled as quickly as we could. I ended up in the master bedroom. I took a sheet off the bed and threw it on the floor. I started with the jewelry first. I found two brand new Rolex watches and a Cuban link chain with, and a couple of medallions. I opened each drawer looking under the folded clothes. I found a few dollars in a money clip, a gun clip, and I saw a few packs of dice. I thought about Monte telling me he was going to teach me how to play one day, so I took those too and put them in my pocket. These dice were special; they were gold.

I went into the closet. That shit was huge. Monte told me one time that people who didn't put money in the bank liked to hide their shit in shoeboxes. Street niggas were creatures of habit and liked to mimic each other. If Eightball and MJG said they hid their money in a Jordan box, then most likely, that's where the money was. I went through every Jordan box, and this nigga Pico seemed to have every pair of Jordan's that ever came out. I flipped one, nothing. Then two, three, four, and on the fifth box, Bingo! Money was wrapped in brown rubber bands. It was too big to fit in my pocket. I felt like taking the box and just leaving, but I couldn't let money come between our friendships. As bad as I wanted to, I didn't. I threw five bundles in the sheet. For some reason, I felt like I was being watched. It was a fucking painting over the bed. I stood on the bed and pulled that shit down. I was getting too paranoid watching him watch me. As I struggled to pull the painting down, I went back to thinking about the friendship I had with Monte and LZ. I wondered if these niggas were as loyal to me as I was to them. When I finally got the painting down, I was shocked at what was behind it—a safe.

"LZ, Monte' come over here!" I yelled.

When they came running into the room, they stopped suddenly, looking up at the large, safe mounted on the wall. I had never seen one up close like this, that shit was cool as fuck to me. It had a large pad, with large bold, black numbers on it.

"How are we gonna get that bitch open?" Monte asked.

He climbed onto the bed, standing next to me. I started pressing random combinations of numbers desperately trying to crack the code but to no avail. Every time I pressed a certain amount of numbers, the pad flashed red, indicating it was the wrong code.

"We can't get that shit open; it's locked. We ain't have time for this dumb shit," LZ said.

He watched us from the bedroom doorway. I took one final crack at it, but it wouldn't budge.

"Come on, Megaman, we got our shit in the hallway," LZ said, then directed his attention to Monte. "Ain't you the one who said five minutes, and we are out?" He looked at Monte.

LZ shook his head, then headed towards the living room. Monte pressed some more numbers before finally jumping off the bed. We all went in the hallway and tied up the sheets that I had. Monte' said the room he went into was a little girl's room.

"She got all the new PlayStation games, and I took that shit. Look what else I got."

He modeled a yellow and white SpongeBob book bag. He paraded it on his shoulder like he had something worth value.

"Stop acting stupid, dumb-ass, we don't have time to play," LZ said seriously. "Let's see what we can put in the bags to try to make it light because we still have to stash everything in the park and come back tonight."

LZ had a roll-out bag that he found. Fortunately for him, the four bricks of cocaine he found in Pico's stash were already neatly packed. LZ stuffed the guns in a large roll-out bag, along with miscellaneous stuff he found. Then I heard something.

"Shut up nigga," LZ said to Monte.

Monte was saying something about looking for more shit, being greedy.

"Did you hear that?" he asked.

I shook my head, yes.

"Heard what?" Monte asked, confused.

"Shhh, shut up," LZ said again.

He dropped his bag, running to the living room. Monte and I squatted down at the same time. I don't know why, because there weren't any windows in the hallway, but it seemed like a safe thing to do. A thought hit me. I opened the sheet I had tied up, frantically searching for jewelry and money. It was right where I thought it would be.

"What are you doing nigga?" Monte asked.

"Shut up nigga, and give me the bag," I replied.

He sucked his teeth.

"You all niggas gonna stop telling me to shut up, my nigga, for real," Monte said.

His eyes got big when I pulled out the bundles of

money. But before he could get a word in, I put my finger to my lips. Then I heard chains on the front door moving. My body froze, but my eyes roamed the hallway waiting for someone to show up. It felt like minutes went by when LZ finally showed up around the corner. He grabbed the bag.

"Come on, they are home. We gotta get the fuck out," LZ said.

"Why the fuck is the lock on the door, Pico? Why the hell can't you get the door open? Shoo, these fucking bags are heavy, nigga."

A woman's voice echoed in the hallway.

"I don't know who put this chain on the door, Boo. Tony probably in the house with a fucking bitch. Yo Tony! Take the chain off the fuckin door, my nigga. This bitch out here trippin," Pico said playfully.

"Pico, don't play with me before I cut your little dick off. Tony ain't in the house, Pico. You forgot I dropped that broke-ass nigga off this morning," she reminded him. Agitated, she rolled her eyes at him.

"OH SHIT!"

That was the last thing I heard going out of the bathroom window headfirst. One of my partners pushed me out, making me fall on the ground, making a loud thud. Monte and LZ were right on my ass. One of the bags flew past my head. I heard footsteps coming up fast in the distance, then shit went from bad to worse.

"Run, nigga run!"

I don't remember who said it, but ain't nobody has to tell me when I heard the shots go off.

'Pop-Pop-Pop.'

This nigga was shooting! We were just young niggas, kids, trying to make a come-up.

I can't die like this.

We made it almost two blocks down behind a building on 183rd that was being renovated. I couldn't breathe. My heart was hurting, it was beating so fast. It felt like it was trying to come out of my chest. I couldn't look back for fear Pico would be standing right behind me.

LZ got rid of one of the backpacks a block ago in this thin grass area that had mud piled underneath it. Monte refused to drop the yellow and white book bag with the famous cartoon character on it. I already knew why.

"Do you fuck niggas think imma let you all get away," Pico yelled in the distance.

He was moving further and further away. We were laid out in a thick brush. In this part of town, it was infested with police, so I knew for a fact, Pico's little search would be called off. We laid in the thick brush, talking about the day's events for at least thirty minutes. When we finally decided to come out of the bushes, I hesitated for a while. Then I jumped over the brush to make sure the coast was clear. Nobody was in sight. Construction workers started to show up for work. The coast was clear, so we thought.

"I gotta go back and get that bag later. We can't tell nobody where it's at either," LZ said.

While he was dusting himself off, I noticed a big red stain on his blue jeans.

"Turn around my nigga," I asked.

I'm sure shock was visible on my face.

"What happened?" he asked.

He started looking around at himself, paranoid. Blood seeped out of his pant leg, where it looked like a hole had been torn in it.

"Oh, my God, I have been shot," he said.

He seemed nonchalant.

"It ain't nothing but a flesh wound, fool. I can't even feel that shit," he said, looking up with a smile.

"You can't walk around these crackers, with blood all over your leg, dummy. You know where we are," I said worriedly.

"I know, but I ain't staying here, and we gotta move together," LZ said.

"Alright, let's just go to the plaza and buy you some new jeans to wear out of the department store," I said.

"With what money?" he asked.

I took the backpack from Monte'. I pulled out the watches and other jewelry and the bundles of money.

"We are rich, bitch!" I said.

There was a jewelry store in the plaza. I figured since we had jewelry, we might as well sell it. Then go to the department store for LZ and figure out what to do next over some lunch. We never made it out of the jewelry store. While the Arab was in the back, checking the value of one of the watches, a policeman walked in. My heart fell to my feet. I thought I saw a police car ride by on the main street earlier but didn't think anything of it because it kept going.

After he called for back-up and an ambulance for LZ, he told us the reason he was in the area. He said someone reported shooting, and he saw three little black kids walking around a shopping plaza alone during school hours. The officer said he would never have stopped us if LZ didn't have the bright red stain on his pants.

"Man, you buzzard as fuck," I told LZ.

We sat in the back seat, handcuffed watching the police spread the contents in the bag on the hood of their car. One of the officers cuffed one of the bundles bravely and walked off.

"That nigga took the money," Monte yelled from the back seat.

"It ain't our nigga, we stole it, remember?" I said.

This was the second time I got trapped with LZ. Now, this was the part I dreaded the most, telling my mother to come to get me from juvenile hall. The charges were minor, being that the nigga Pico never reported the shit.

When I called home, nobody answered. My case manager said if nobody picked up the phone within the next twenty minutes, that she was going home, and I was going to juvenile hall. She said that if I went to juvenile hall, I would have to be arraigned in the morning by a judge to see what they wanted to do. I called home again. My Aunt Ket-Ket picked up and called me everything in the book, except Jesus. She told me she wasn't coming to get me, and I had to wait until my mom came home from the hospital. She had just had a baby.

She drilled me about stressing my mom out, saying how my mother was only seven months pregnant, and because of me, she was having the baby early. I listened to her go on and on about this baby stuff. I kept thinking, why the fuck was I even listening to this woman? If she wasn't coming to get me, we didn't need to be talking. The last thing I heard before I hung up was, "Kahi…"

KP ended up getting his cut. While we were in jail, LZ called him and told him where the other bag was. He promised us that he would lookout, which I doubted.

CHAPTER SEVENTEEN

Francia Marie Guierra was born on August 21, 1998. They named my baby sister Francia after my great grandma. My sister's middle name is also my Aunt Marie's first name.

At the time, I was stuck in a one-man cell occupied by six other people. There were two-inch-thick concrete slabs against the far wall that sat across from each other. They both had thin mats and a stained sheet on each. All the other mats were lined up on the floor from the entrance door to the wall in the back. There was a tight walkway. The only thing you could do once you walked in the room was get straight in your bunk. The toilet and sink were together. The other six boys and I used the bathroom one after another when each meal was served. At times when we couldn't hold it, we would use the bathroom simultaneously and do one big flush.

When I was bored, I would pace the square in the room by the front door back and forth and couldn't do that without stepping on someone's mat. We killed time telling stories. It ain't like I could talk to Monte and them. They were in a different range that was on the other side of the building. A Dominican kid from Overtown named Stanka knew how to make dice with toilet paper. We shot dice for honey buns on the breakfast tray, which I won every morning. Since it came in plastic, that was all I could eat off that nasty-ass tray.

My mother refused to come to get me thanks to my Aunt Ket-Ket's influence. She had the nerve to call my case manager, telling her that I needed a program for my behavior. I felt like that was my Aunt's idea, since she always brought it up to my mom whenever she heard I was in trouble. I started to feel claustrophobic after the first week. All the guys went home after the first two weeks, and I ended up in the cell all by myself. Being in the cell alone was driving me crazy. I thought of the craziest shit. It wasn't like getting locked up and going home, this shit was for real, and my mind pulled me in a hundred different directions.

When they finally came to get me, the bulge in her stomach had begun to subside. I could tell she was still mad at what the judge told her.

"Mr. Guierra is not eligible to stay in the confines of the juvenile justice system. He has no prior violence that deems him a threat to society, and um…" he took a moment to gather himself.

"I strongly believe this is an issue that his parents can resolve through counseling and effective parenting. I'm going to give Mr. Guierra twenty-one days served. Today you can go home, Mr. Guierra," the judge said, peeling my skin off with his sharp stare.

I stood at the podium with my mother and court-appointed lawyer quiet as a church mouse. I wanted to jump for joy when the judge said something about going home. All that other shit went in one ear and out the other. But he wasn't finished!

"Ms. Guierra, I can see the frustration written all over your face. I recommend you take that boy home and teach his butt a lesson!"

At that point, my mom and I looked at each other. She couldn't hide her frustration. This man was giving her a pass to beat my ass like she didn't already have a license to do so. On the drive home, she still kept silent. I sat in the back seat to avoid that post-court drama as if watching me through the rear-view mirror wasn't enough torture.

I held my baby sister for the first time. She was white as hell, her little pink fingers reaching for the bottle that I cradled in her mouth. She wasn't strong enough to hold it on her own yet, so I guided her. My mother taught me to treat the women in my own family like queens, so that's what I was doing.

As the oldest, and having two sisters to look after, there was a lot on my plate. Francia had a full head of curly hair. She inherited grandma's marble-brown eyes and had a small mole on the top right side of her face. She looked like my mother a lot, but with my mother being a light-skinned woman and her father being a light-skinned man, Francia looked like a little white baby.

After I fed her and talked to Simon for a while about my whole juvenile experience, I went to take a shower. For the past couple of weeks at the juvenile, I was only allowed one shower a day, and half the time, that shit was cold.

I finally got out of Jann Mann. I kept up with academic stuff and passed on to ninth grade. I still had a monkey on my back; let my aunt tell it.

Not long after I was back in the system, this time for more serious shit, I became a habitual juvenile offender. That was unheard of amongst my peers. I had been charged as petty as burglary that escalated to arm robbery. Amongst other shit, I was glad that Simon decided he should get us a family lawyer, so I could beat a few charges and wouldn't have to sit more than a week at some events.

"Them shits clean bro. What size do you wear, nigga?' LZ asked, looking down at my Nike Flights.

I bought them myself since I started selling a little weed to the neighborhood kids in Greynolds Park. I found out that the square kid, Jason, who stayed across the street, had a connect that didn't even care for. He introduced me to his friend named JB, short for Jordan something. I couldn't even pronounce the kid's last name.

The kid grew his weed in his backyard, and his parents allowed him to. He was a pure weed head and didn't care to make any money. He just wanted to smoke it all. He was the connect for any kind of weed I wanted. So, with a little convincing, I got him to serve me as one of his clients. I went in my stash from all the licks we did. I still had rainy-day money from my days of B&E's with Monte' and LZ. It was on after that.

I gave him money, and he brought me the shit. He even showed me how to bag them to make five-dollar bags look fatter than they were. He was in the habit of smoking, and I was in the business of profiting. I like to smoke too, but the money came first. Besides, I was taught that you never get high on your own supply. Since my mother told me she wasn't getting me shit for my first day of school until I stopped getting in trouble, it made me go out and get it myself.

"They are your size nigga," I said, smiling. "I was tryna get the red and black Flights, but they don't have my size, so I got the all-white ones. Where is everybody at, though? I ain't seen Monte or none of the boys." I asked him.

LZ stared, admiring my shoes.

"They are around here, trust me. This shit is deep too. All the broads are out here," LZ said, looking around.

We stood there for a while, peeping at the scenery. Random people came up, some gave us dap, and others walked by in envy. It was all the same playbook to me. I was used to people hating from the outside. It never bothered me once, until they brought the pressure to our front door.

"You know Pouchon lying ass is out. He is around here chasing Farrah."

"Are you talking about little skinny Farrah?" I asked. "The last time I saw her, she was rail thin."

"She ain't skinny no more, fool, little mama is now super fine," he said, still looking at the crowd.

"You are bullshitting, that's crazy. You all niggas haven't seen Danielle or Avi? Have you seen her yet?" I questioned.

"Yeah, Avia is around, she is looking good too. I might have to try that," he said, throwing his set up at me playfully.

"Stop playing silly nigga," I said seriously.

He knew I had a spot for Avia.

"Avia asked for you recently, though. Danielle said she wasn't coming to this high school, she transferred to another school. Monkey Red stupid ass still goes out here though, you should ask her what's up with Danielle."

"Danielle isn't bugging, fool. Why the hell would she pass up NMB and go somewhere else? This is a fashion school, and she loves that type of shit. Fuck it, I'm out to find Avia ass right quickly. Imma talk to you later, kid. If you see Monte tell that nigga to scream at me."

"Alright, fool. Hey crocodile, check this out yo," he yelled after a girl, playfully.

When she looked back and saw who it was, she took off running. He took off after her. I just shook my head and kept walking.

"Cuze me, girl, can you get out of my way?" I said, brushing past Avia.

"Don't play with me, boy," she yelled back. "Damn, that nigga is rude," she reckoned.

When I turned around, the look on her face was pure anger. Every time I saw this girl, she was upbeat, and it always took a little disrespect to get her out of character. When she realized who was staring back at her, her face started to soften up.

"Who were you talking to with your funny looking self?" I said, smiling.

"Nigga," she said, biting her words.

"You said nigga, Mrs. Smith. I have never heard you use such profane language," I said, imitating someone who spoke properly.

"Mahkahi, oh my goodness, boy shut up and give me a hug," she said.

Avia put me in a bear hug. I was shocked. I never once touched this girl. I didn't know how I should've hugged her, so I just put my arms around her neck.

"What's good, woman? You have grown the past couple of months, but you still a midget, though," I said, comparing her height to mine.

I had grown myself. I was taller, stronger, and my cinnamon-bronze skin took its natural color back. Running the streets all day made my skin appear darker. Since being released from juvenile, I got out, and I glowed a little more. Between doing push-ups and growing mentally, it made me a different type of young nigga—a more mature one.

"Boy, you are looking good too," she said.

Her statement caught me off guard again.

"I heard you got in trouble, and they kicked you out of JFK. After that, I never saw you no more. I didn't think you were coming out to NMB for high school."

"How could I stay away too long? Girl, you're my other half," I said.

The people she was with started to laugh. Avia blushed, patting me on the arm.

"Boy, you are still funny," she said. "Oh, my bad. These are my friends. Lisa, this Mahkahi, Mahkahi, this is Lisa."

I nodded my head towards Lisa.

"And this is Keisha. Keisha, this is Mahkahi."

I nodded towards Keisha. Both girls were fine, but not better looking than my future girl.

"I'm glad I ran into you. I wanted to talk to you about something, but not here. Let me check in with my classes, and maybe we can have lunch together or something," I said.

I was hopeful that she wouldn't turn me down.

"Lunch, ok, no problem Mahkahi. Where do you want to meet?" she questioned.

"I don't even know this school like that but meet me in front of the school on the sidewalk by the stairs."

"Don't have me out there all day Mahkahi," she said seriously.

"See you at lunchtime," she blushed.

"You know you don't have to say my whole first name, you can call me what everybody else calls me."

"Megaman? For what? I like your name, it's different," she said, turning around to leave.

I love the way you say it, too, I thought to myself.

I stood in front of the school for a while. People came and went, but there was no sign of Avia.

"Ah shit, there goes my nigga," I heard a familiar voice say.

Monte came up behind me and tried to scoop me up.

"Damn my nigga, you have gained some weight, fool.

Fuck have you been eating?" he said, putting me back down.

"It's Haitian food my grandma Nah-Nah has been making, you already know."

"Yeah, Nah-Nah can throw down. I miss that good food. The lady got one good arm, and she still does her thing. I ain't coming around here till your old girl calms down, though. She ain't feeling a nigga right now," he said.

My mother found out he was the one with me, along with LZ, that day we got locked up.

"We are back out here, though, fool! We're gonna be straight in a minute. But you look like you already hit the ground running," he stepped back to take a good look at my outfit and shoes.

"You right, but imma put you on what I have been working on. This is a whole different ball game."

"Alright, we'll talk, but I know you can't wait till you get one of these high school hoes under your belt," he said.

What he didn't know was I already had a couple under my belt, literally.

After fucking with Angelica, my name ran amongst her friends. I knocked two or three of them off behind her back. When she found out, she called herself, cutting me off for a while. She was still coming around even after my mother told her she didn't need her anymore since grandma Nah-Nah was always there. I almost fucked up when I threw a condom wrapper in the bathroom garbage. My mom assumed Simon was fucking another bitch when she found it. I told Simon it was mine, but he kept it between us. My mom was mad for a little while but got over it.

"Yeah, I can't wait, I said, clasping my hands together."

"Curse me, fool," Avia said, trying to disguise her voice.

Monte went to grab her shirt, but I grabbed his arm. When she turned around, she had this big smirk on her face.

"I saw you standing here, I was just letting you two get done with your little conversation," she said. "Hey Monte', how are you doing, boy?"

"I'm good. I'm good. Check this out though, I'm tryna slide, imma catch you married people later. By the way, you two look so good together," he said, leaving.

We looked at each other, facing off. Avia just burst out laughing. I didn't think it was that funny because, for some reason, I wanted Avia to be in my life forever.

"Let's walk to the Spanish restaurant up the street. I'm hungry as hell. I think we still got like twenty minutes for lunch," I instructed.

As we walked, we talked about everything and anything we could think of. Her company made me feel comfortable. She had a natural sense of humor. She told me jokes, and we cracked on people along the way. I still hadn't told her what I wanted to say, but I planned to soon as we got our food.

I ordered red beans with rice, fillet chicken, and a side salad.

"I'll just get the same thing he is getting ma'am, thank you," she told the waitress.

"Would you like anything to drink?" the waitress asked.

"Lemonade," we said in unison.

All of us laughed at that one.

After the waitress walked away, I said, "Avia, imma get straight to the point. I've liked you since mid…"

"Here's your drink, Papi," the Spanish woman came back, putting the drinks on our saucers.

Damn, she was fast.

The way she gave me a welcoming look set Avia in a bad mood.

"Thank you," I said, holding her gaze.

She had these inviting dark brown eyes that looked right through me. Then she licked her lips seductively. When I looked over at Avia, she rolled her eyes at both of us. Whether the girl noticed or not, I don't think she really cared.

"Listen, Avia, you need to make this," I said, pointing from her to me and me to her. "Official. I've liked you since middle school. I think you know that, and I know you like me, right? You do like me, right?" I asked sarcastically.

"I do, Mahkahi, but I don't know about you and all these other girls. Besides, I mess with Bizzy, and I kind of like him. Don't get me wrong, I like you too, Kahi, but you are a dog, boy, and I can't go through that with you. I saw the way that lady looked at you, and it seems like she had a thing with you too," she said, rolling her neck.

My heart was crushed. All I heard was *'mess with Bizzy.'* All that other shit I could account for because I was sloppy for some reason. I wondered if she had sex with Bizzy, but I didn't want to come out and just ask.

"So, you two are official then?" I asked.

"No, we ain't official, he wants to make it that. The same thing I see in him, I see in you."

"Hold that thought, little mama. I'm in a class of my own. You might see me tripping around here, but at the same time, I like you and only you. Don't compare me to that nigga. Just give me some thought. What do you think?" I asked seriously.

"I think I might just eat my food and tell you later," Avia said with an attitude.

The pretty Hispanic woman returned with our food.

She laid my tray in front of me, and she tried to set Avia's plate in front of her, but Avia snatched it out of her hand. Avia gave her a look that could poke holes through her skin.

We ate in silence, glancing at each other every now and then. When we were finished, we called the woman over to pay for our meal. When I reached in my pocket, Avia stopped me.

"Hold up Mahkahi, let me take care of that for us."

I picked the paper up before she could reach it, looking at the tab. It was eighteen dollars.

She reached over and snatched it out of my hand, looked at it, and gave the woman a twenty-dollar bill. "Keep the change, ma'am," she said with a smile like she did the woman a favor.

I liked women like Avia. She was one of those girls I wasn't used to.

I planned on making her my girl by any means. I didn't give it a thought that she might have known some of those girls I fucked with. And the thought of her messing with Bizzy made me sick to the stomach. I had to play my position.

When we got back to school, we exchanged numbers and embraced them. She kissed me lightly on the cheek before we went our separate ways. She was already letting me know I held a spot, but I just had to earn it. I couldn't wait to tell Monte how she paid for our food.

CHAPTER EIGHTEEN

Norwood was in Carol City, but not exactly. They called Norwood the backyard of Carol City because you have to go through Norwood, no matter where you came from, to get to the heart of Carol City. My mom had found a bigger house in the area and planned on moving us out soon. But I didn't know when, and I really didn't want to take her seriously. I was comfortable where we were.

Shit had gotten crazy in Victory Park. The War between UP and VP boys had become fierce. To me, those niggas weren't worth the beef because they weren't doing the shit we were doing. They weren't making money. I felt like it was a waste of time. Washington Park niggas were getting money, and we weren't beefing them. I know with money comes jealousy, and that's what all this shit is about.

As the beef escalated, our brotherhood got tighter. We didn't let any of our group members go out alone without having one of us as an escort. We had to watch each other's backs. We shared hos, clothing, and joints. The only exception was my main girl, who I wasn't trying to share. The main chicks got a pass, we all agreed on that. But everything else goes. 'It ain't no fun if the homie can't have any,' was my motto.

My relationship with LZ grew far beyond friendship. Nobody could tell we weren't related. We were all we had, and it was a relationship I valued like he was my brother. I took him and his family as my own. I got to know LZ's two other brothers. Lil Trigga has a mean left hand that he was

not scared to use. He was the youngest of the four brothers, and very spoiled. Six fingers were the oldest but act
immature for his age. He earned that nickname from the
extra pinky finger he had on his left hand. He is the black
sheep of his family, and they would jump on his ass for the
dumbest shit.

LZ favored his father the most, they both were short
and stocky. His father was strict and was an asshole all
the time. The only person I saw LZ's father with besides
his family was Nief, his brother, and his co-worker. And
most times, if they weren't fishing, they were working. His
mom, Ms. Robiou, accepted me as one of her own, and I
will always be indebted to her because of that.

LZ and I were so much alike that it didn't make sense.
Even though we hit a few bumps along the road, and
crashed a couple of times, we made up on the back end. The
rules were something we defied. "S.T.O.P" meant "GO" to
us, and we broke the rules every chance we got.

After a few months of protest, my mom had made up
her mind about moving. She wasn't ready to listen to me.

"Ma, you moved us out of Lil Haiti so we could be comfortable here, and we are. Why are we moving again?" I
whined on our way to the new house, trying to convince her.

She wanted me to go with her so she could sign some
papers and show me how serious she was.

"Kahi, the house is bigger, and grandma Nah-Nah
needs more space to move around. This house is better,
trust me, you'll like it," she explained.

"This ain't fair, though, ma. I like the house we are at
now. You keep moving and moving every time I get settled. I got friends here and I attend a school I like," I blurted
out, half-mad but careful not to cross the line.

"What is it to you, Kahi? And you better not talk to me

like I'm not trying to build a better life for you and your sisters. You know how hard I work so you can get the shit you'll want. Are you talking about new friends? New friends, huh? Those little hoodlums you call friends, running the streets all day, sagging their pants off their ass. Friends? Is that what you call them? Do you know where that sagging shit came from? Sissies in jail, so that another man can claim their property.

Do you know what jail is? You can't keep out of jail because of your so-called friends. You act like you are living a double life at my house. I don't want any phone calls talking about you dead or about you killing somebody. I'm tired, Kahi," she sighed.

"I know, ma, but what if I don't get in trouble no more?" I asked.

"You said that the last five times you went to juvenile," she reminded me.

"Ma, please come get me. Ma, I won't get in trouble anymore. Ma, I did nothing. Me and my friends…. Me and my friends…" she mimicked me.

"I don't want to hear that crap. You have two little sisters to look after. Kadisha is growing, Kahi. I don't want any negative stuff around my babies."

"Damn, ma, you act like I can't get in trouble wherever we go. It doesn't matter. You just want to move because you want to move. You act like you don't want to see me happy," I retorted. I plopped on the passenger seat. She pulled over into the median and turned to face me.

"Don't you fucking dare mess with me!" she yelled, putting her finger in my face.

"I will slap the shit out of you if you ever disrespect me like that again," she growled while poking me on the side of my head with her long nails.

"This ain't just about you, Mahkahi. It's about us. You'll understand that one day, but right now, you don't get it because you don't have no responsibilities.

"Sorry, mama," I said.

I crossed my arms over my chest as tears rolled down my face. No matter how wrong, I felt my mother was, I would never disrespect her. She is my mother.

"I'm taking your ass out of sorry ass NMB too and putting you in Norland Senior High. It's only a couple blocks from the house," she emphasized.

Norland Senior High was full of Jamaicans and other island people. It wasn't a fashion school like NMB, but it could come in number five of the top schools in Dade County. I wasn't feeling the idea of having to switch schools, but I didn't protest. I had my own means of getting back to the V, so I didn't care anymore like I did initially. I would find my way back to NMB. My first plan was to buy a bike, so I could get around. I watched the route to and fro; it was simple. It only took five minutes by car. On a bike, it will take like ten minutes.

When we pulled up at the house, it looked like the whole work was already done for us. A woman stood beside a man with a clipboard in his hands. They welcomed us with all smiles. They showed us the whole yard first. The front yard was alright, better looking than the first time I saw our current house. We went out back, and the woman pointed to the dog kennel the previous owners had built. She said that the house was dog friendly. We rounded the whole yard and ended up going inside through the front door.

The living room was spacious, the white tile was glistening under the chandelier like it had just been waxed. Diamond-shaped mirrors in different sizes lined the walls going around in a perfect circle. There must have been a dozen mirrors with designs on top and around them, some tall for full-body view, and some short for the upper body view. I was feeling the layout, but I still wasn't feeling the move.

I was just starting to adapt to NMB, the whole area, and this shit happened. Avia and I started talking more and had finally made it official. I sealed the deal one day when she was walking with Bizzy in a crowded hallway on the way to class. When she saw me going in the opposite direction, she followed me, leaving Bizzy all alone. The look on his face was to die for. I needed to build my ego.

I took that nigga's chick.

Since one rainy day I gave Avia my black snoopy sweater, she wore it every day to school. Bizzy no longer wanted her. She told me she asked him to still be friends, but he declined. Every day after school, we met up on the back bridge. It was another shortcut to the V; I didn't know about it. It was a backroad Monte showed me. There is a short cut in the public library that leads to the famous one way. I saw opportunities we could take advantage of with that shortcut. However, in the meantime, I had to find a way to tell Avia and the fellas I was moving.

When I told Avia, she wasn't happy, but she wasn't tripping either. I guess it was because she wanted me to stay out of trouble as much as my mom did. She got on the internet and researched a public transportation route so that we could still visit each other.

"Where you'll moving to?" LZ asked after I broke the news to him.

"Norland and she is talking about transferring me to Norland Senior High. I tried to plead my case, but she caught onto me," I said, defeated.

"It is nothing. It isn't like you are moving to the other side of the world. Shit, we might have to set up shop around the dreads, feel me?" LZ said, dapping me up. "We all got this, fam. Don't get there and start speaking "bomboclaude" and shit," he stated, laughing, and doing a fake-ass Jamaican dance.

"We got some dog kennels at the back of the house, like seven cages. I know you like to keep dogs. I need to check with my old girl, though,' I told him.

"Damn Monte, you still ain't roll that shit up, yet?" I asked, shifting my attention to Monte.

He was in deep thought, trying to roll the joint for the third time. He never got it down pat. That's something he just couldn't get right.

"Hey D, roll us one up, this nigga has been sitting here for 30 minutes tryna roll one damn joint," I said, signaling Big D to come my way.

He was at the bridge talking to some broad and threw his finger up, telling us to hold on.

We sat around talking. I told them all the shit that I saw in the area and how the layout was. Big D said that's where he was staying before he moved to the V, so he knew that shit like the back of his hand. Moving into all these strange places, I couldn't get used to anywhere. I had to learn to adapt everywhere I went, and that seemed to be one of my strengths.

The only real change in staying in Norland that I made from the last time we moved was who I associated myself with. I wasn't jumping from click to click, and my loyalty was to the hand that fed me, which was VP. My first day at Norland Senior High was a pain in the ass. They had the classroom numbers set up in backward rotation, all over the place, and in wings from A to D.

"Where is room 187, fool?" I asked a big kid wearing an Adidas starter's jacket in 100-degree weather.

Had I not looked up; he would have sped past me in the packed hallway. There was traffic coming from both ends, and fast.

"To the left, pass the chow hall," he said.

He looked down at me, then disappeared into the crowd.

Walking towards my first-period class, I had my head down reading the paper that had all my classes lined up in order, while looking up occasionally at the numbers on the door. I couldn't figure out how this shit worked. People bumped into me from all corners, nobody said excuse me. I felt like a running back in a homecoming game, trying to score a touchdown walking through a crowded hallway.

I looked at the paper confused because it read 187, but when I stopped to look at the numbers on the doors, they went from 188 to 186, but no 187. I tried to follow the same trail Big Kid sent me but to no avail.

I was starting to get frustrated. I tried to get someone else's attention, but the people around me were speeding like I wasn't even there. I stood there looking around aimlessly. I saw this kid walking past me, facing the other way. He looked familiar. I thought I recognized him but pushed the thought out until I saw this fine-ass yellow bone with some hip-hugging pants on. Her body screamed for attention. When we locked eyes, I flashed a smile with the new gold crowns I had on my fangs. She just nodded her head in approval, smiling back at me, and kept moving. I took a mental picture, reminding myself to bag that. I followed her curvaceous body with lust. She seemed like a challenge I was willing to take.

As soon as I looked up, I noticed the same kid I thought

I knew, looking dead in my face. It was my cousin, Uno. I hadn't seen Uno in a long time, probably since elementary school. My mother had a fall out with his mother after my father got shot. Freshman year in high school, and this nigga Uno already got a full beard. He resembled a black wolf.

"Damn Kahi, what's good little nigga? How is ya old girl holding up, fool?" He asked after shaking me.

"Lil Nigga?" I asked, sizing him up.

He was a little bigger than me and grew a beard over the years, but we were the same age.

"What the fuck are you talking about, cuzzo? Nigga, we are the same age. I'm good, though. The old girl moved here. Other than that, she still the same, working hard," I replied.

"What's up with Nichole's crazy-ass? How is she holding up? Because the last time I saw auntie, she was still acting like she was twenty-one. That's why I loved your mama. She was down to earth, fool. She ain't like them other Haitians," I reasoned.

"Nichole still being Nichole, messy as hell. Still acting twenty years younger, after all these years. When was the last time I saw you? Like elementary school? You still look the same too. Just like your daddy. What are you doing out here, though? Last time I heard, you were staying in NMB."

"My old girl just got on some other shit too. We have been in NMB since we moved from Lil Haiti. She just had a little girl recently, and grandma Nah-Nah came to stay with us. She felt the crib we were staying in was not comfortable for all of us, so we moved up here," I replied.

"Where did you'll stay at in NMB? Uno asked curiously.

"Greynolds Park, down the street from the V."

"I know a few niggas in the V," he said, nodding his head approvingly.

"I will catch up with you later, cousin. I got a couple moves to make really quick," I said, cutting the conversation short. "Make sure you catch up with me after school. I'll meet you around the patio, we could talk then." I reasoned before walking away.

"Alright, kid," he replied and walked in the opposite direction.

As I got further away, I thought about it for a second, he might know where the classroom is.

"Hey, Uno," I yelled down the hallway. "Yo, boy."

I yelled again. When he finally turned around, I jogged halfway towards his direction.

"Where is room 187 at, fool?" I asked impatiently.

I was new here and already couldn't stand the way it was set up.

"It's like four doors around that corner. The number ain't even on top of the door. They got these hallways all fucked up. These lazy motherfuckers never fixed the shit."

With that, we parted ways.

CHAPTER NINETEEN

I ended up liking Norland. I convinced LZ to get his mother to transfer him to Norland using our address, and Ace followed suit. Lil V did the same when he finally got out of Jann Mann. Monte and Big D were on some 'fuck school type of shit. Not long after that, we all followed suit.

My pussy rate just kept shooting up. It seemed like the more pussy I got, and the more money I made, I was feeling like Monte and others. FUCK SCHOOL!

My mother ended up changing her night shift to the day shift. Simon started a good job with his sister in a tile business she owned and was always at work during the day. Grandma Nah-Nah fell ill again and ended up in the hospital for a couple of weeks. That left me with more than enough idle time.

I had to walk to middle school to get Disha every day at 4:00 p.m. With everybody gone all day, I had the house to myself from 7:00 a.m. to 4:00 p.m.

I taxed niggas from my block and niggas from the school to pay me for an hour in the boom-boom room. It seemed like everywhere I went, I marked my territory. I could only make a few appointments throughout the day, depending on how long I knew it took someone to get their rocks off. Of course, the more I got to know some dudes, I was able to work out all the kinks.

"That'll be ten dollars an hour," I would say when my clients came knocking, and they had to pay upfront.

These lames paid ten dollars for an hour but would probably be in the boom-boom room for half the time. Some people just wanted to get freaky really quickly and walk back to school. It was a win-win hustle. I got money, they caught a nut, and everybody was happy.

"Where is the bread at, Megaman? I'm hungry," Ace asked, coming out of my room with his shirt off.

Today was an easy day, and I was in chill mode. I only had three people coming by. I was in the living room playing 007 with Kato, while Uno watched it. Uno and Kato were mutual friends. Kato is the one who almost got his head bashed in at a dice game with Monte's older brother. I found out Uno knew more than a few niggas in Victory Park, so it was all love. Kato was up to his old ways, and I fell right into his trap.

"On the third cabinet from your right, by the fridge," I said, without looking up at him.

All I had to do was look in the mirror on the wall in front of me on top of the television. Ace was on 'borrowed time.' I couldn't charge my nigga for a broad all of us just fucked. We all just took turns tearing a new pussy hole in this chick, thanks to me. I put my dick game down, then talked her into giving the goodies if she wanted to stay in the house. The only way that was going to happen was if she let my dawgs have fun too. She agreed, but Ace was in there lollygagging. We were so lost in the game, Uno had to bring it to our attention.

"Damn kid, you are in there making a movie, aren't you? You act like you are making love to the broad," Uno said to Ace while heading to the kitchen, loud enough for Kato and me to hear.

He wasn't the only one making love. The other dude and girl who paid me for an hour had been in the room past the time I predicted. I had another appointment coming in ten minutes, so they were about to get kicked the fuck out.

"Man, that pussy has some fire. I need to fuel-up for round three," he yelled back from the kitchen.

"Nigga, you better not be thinking about kissing that bitch if you already did, because you might taste my dick," that comment made us all laugh, even Ace.

"Nah nigga, I ain't done none of that." He said, walking past us with two cups and a sandwich.

"Hey Megaman, what the fuck is this nigga doing taking two cups to the room? Is he a personal servant or something?" Uno asked.

I looked through the mirror.

"What nigga, you tripping? Yo Ace. Check me out, fool," I yelled as he flew into the room.

My eyes fell back on the screen.

Kato had me down forty bucks, and I was trying to get back at least twenty of them. All those distractions frustrated me.

"Gotcha ass nigga, come here," Kato said, talking to me and looking at the screen.

At the same time, the front door came open. I didn't even get to say what was on my mind. It was my mother!

The look on her face registered shock. I just looked up at her knowing there was no way I was going to be able to explain this. I was caught with my hands in the cookie jar. It was only eleven in the morning; she wasn't due back for another six hours. I blinked once, and she was right up on me. I cowered defensively, thinking she was going to strike, but she went past me tearing at the television. She started fiddling for the PlayStation cords, ripping everything off. Kato jumped out of the way as she snatched the controller by the cord, pulling it right out of his hand. I had already dropped mine. Uno was already by the front door, but he wasn't gone yet.

"So ti la!" Fout soti la devou pot mwen an!," (Get out! Get the fuck out of my house), she yelled.

She was still holding the game console, with wires dangling in her hands while heading to the front door. She threw them out. She was mad, very mad. I knew this because she just bought me all that shit with her money. She came back into the house, looking around the living room like a mad black woman.

"I came home, thinking I could get some sleep. I feel sick. And your ass is supposed to be at school. But here you are with your gang? Is this what you do with your time? Have all your goons in my fucking house, eating up my shit?" she yelled, referring to the dirty plate on the floor in the living room.

"Nick, you know better, you know better than to be around him doing this," she said, pointing to Uno.

She made it seem like I was a bad influence. Uno was already in the streets from what I knew. But ever since I told her he was going to high school, she allowed him to come and go as he pleased. He put on a good front like he was an angel.

"Bon Dieu edem mwen!" (Lord help me) she said, laughing sarcastically.

"Who the fuck is you? And you? You little bitches should be ashamed of yourselves. "Soti la! Fout soti la devou pot mwen an," (Get out! Get the fuck out of my house) she continued to scream in creole.

The girls looked at her like she was crazy. Ace hung his head low, and the other buddy did the same. They hurried past her and got out like they were told. When she walked away to a safe distance, I ran out of the house like a bat out of hell. She tried to call me back, but I was already halfway down the block. I didn't think twice about looking back. Kato had a splaq (stolen car) around the block. Kato jumped into the driver's seat. He had the music turned up to the max. Uno had been playing with the music for a while and told Kato and me to bump his latest song, "Trap House."

Kato didn't even give me a chance to answer when he said, "Let me get them ten dollars you owe me, nigga. Imma just go ahead and put that in the tank."

I looked at him like he was out of his cotton-picking mind.

"Nigga, were you not just at the house? Did you see what the fuck just happened? And you are asking about ten ass dollars? Not right now," I said seriously. "Technically, though, I didn't lose that last dime. You were lucky I didn't win all my shit back. Besides, she fucked the game up when she pulled the cord out of the back of the TV, "I said seriously. My head started to hurt from all the stress I had just been through.

"I'm fucking with you, kid. I just needed my witnesses to know I beat your tough ass," he said, smiling.

I should have known better than to gamble against Kato. That was his niche. He got off on gambling.

"That shit back there, though, Megaman. I thought your old girl was gonna try and stunt one of us. I ran to clean up that bitch," he continued to say.

"Who are you telling, fool? I need to figure out what I wanna tell her when I get back to the crib. My head is hurting right now. She is gonna get my ass when I get back," I said.

The thought of coming home made my head pound in fear. Eventually, I still had to go back home. I needed to give her some time to cool off.

"Your mama still whoop you, boy?" Ace said, laughing in the back seat.

"Whoop, nigga, that's an understatement, she goes for the kill. My mama grabs anything she can find to beat ya ass when her fist gets sore. That little lady doesn't play no games, bro," I said, remembering the last time she hit me.

I touched my shoulder subconsciously, where she left a bruise.

"Fool, I don't know how you gonna fix that one," Uno said, shaking his head.

"I don't know either, fool," I replied.

Ace had fired up a joint, as it went around in rotation. I was thinking about the disappointed look on my mama's face. I kept getting caught up in my recklessness. I didn't want to know what the outcome of this mess was going to be. My mind began to drift off to LaLa land. I was so high, everything around me was one big cloud I wish I could sleep on for the rest of the night.

I came home late after spending the night running around the neighborhood. Kato left in the car that was supposed to be my ride back home. It got too late to just wait around, so I had to find my own way. It was around 10:00 pm. I was supposed to be home way before then, and the late bus was out of the question. I had to get home fast and now. LZ said Six fingers had a beach cruiser that he brought home. He said I couldn't take it with me, so he would ride me on the handlebars. Then my bad day turned worse as it started to rain. LZ looked at me as we stood getting soaked by the cold rainwater. I said, "Fuck it," and we set out to get me home.

"Alright, bro, it was nice knowing you, kid," LZ said, dropping me off down the street from my house.

He knew what it felt like to feel the wrath of my mother,

and he wanted no part of it. Our clothes were soaking wet from the rain. I felt sticky and needed a shower badly.

"Imma be alright, playa, it isn't like she is gonna kill me. You don't think she'll kill me, do you?" I asked him jokingly but somewhat seriously.

I didn't know what my mother was capable of. I shivered, not knowing if it was because of the cool breeze or the mere thought of my mother's wrath. I was caught red-handed and felt both embarrassed and regretful. Embarrassed because I got caught and regretful because it was my mom who caught me and not Simon.

I felt a little guilty about bringing people to her house. But damn, a nigga was just stretching his wings. It ain't like I wasn't making money or like I was going to jail for being in my own house. I bit more than I could chew, and as much as I liked to prolong my thoughts, I had to go there to the Haitian lady.

"Nah," LZ said, answering me. "But if she does, call me," he said, spinning the bike back around in the direction we came from.

"Ooops, my bad! You won't because she might kill ya ass," he screamed before leaving.

LZ and I's friendship was inseparable. I was grateful for him looking out, but it was time to face the music.

I went around the side of the house, over by Kadisha's room, and knocked on her window, hoping she would get up and open the door. She was a hard sleeper, so she didn't hear me. I walked around the backyard and noticed that my mom's bedroom light was still on.

"What the fuck is she still doing up? Damn, man!" I mumbled to myself.

I checked the bathroom window next, the sliding door, and then the laundry room, which had a door that led inside the house. All of them were locked. She wasn't slipping like that. I only had one choice, the front door.

"I got to go there anyway. Fuck it, what do I have to lose?" I said, hyping myself up.

I reached out for the door, and it snatched open before I could knock.

"Where are you coming from?" she asked seriously.

The demeanor in her voice was subtle like she was tired. Her purse hung on her shoulders like she was on her way out. I assumed she was going to find me. I looked at the clock on the wall, and it was almost eleven.

"I was at Emmanuel and Dem's house," I said, referring to LZ's real name.

I looked down at the doormat. I could feel her eyes piercing through me. She let out a hard cough making me look at her face. The worrisome look I saw rubbed me the wrong way like she knew something I didn't.

Probably because I drove her half-crazy, I thought.

"I was just coming to look for you. You are out there in the rain. Boy, what am I going to do with you?" She asked.

I didn't say anything.

"I'm too tired to deal with this right now, Kahi. I'll talk to you tomorrow," she said and stepped aside.

She let me into the house, before marching back to her bedroom.

I walked into my house, my head hanging low in shame. I went into my room, took all my wet clothes off, and prepared myself a long hot bath. I let the steam beat on my wavy hair. I kept thinking something was wrong, but I couldn't put my finger on it. I just thought to myself that I needed to make this right.

CHAPTER TWENTY

Grandma Nah-Nah ended up having another stroke and went back to the hospital for a while. Doctors said that she was careless with her health and that she was lucky to still be alive. Auntie Ket-Ket, Kadisha, Simon, and I were on our way to see her at the hospital since my mom was bed-ridden for a week now. That day she told me she was feeling sick and it ended up being the beginning of her long term illness. We all played our part in taking care of my mom.

As the days went by, she was too sick to visit Grandma at the hospital, so Simon offered to take us to her. For a few weeks, all my mom could do was lay in bed. I stepped up and started doing little things to help her out. I made phone calls to the hospital checking up on Grandma Nah-Nah. I made mom hot soups and did anything she asked me to. Shit, I was going to do anything to stay on her good side. The last time I checked on Grandma Nah-Nah, the doctor told me her condition had worsened, and that she would have to stay admitted until her condition improved. The way my mother's face contorted when I told her, I couldn't tell if it was from pain or the news of Grandma Nah-Nah.

We waited outside of Auntie Ket-Ket's house in North Miami, but she never came out. Simon got impatient waiting for her because we had to be at the hospital before the visiting time was over. Simon went inside to get her while Disha and I sat in the car talking. I tried to explain to her what was happening, and she hit me with twenty-one questions.

"Is Nah-Nah gonna get so sick that she could die?" Kadisha asked curiously.

The question was a deep one that I hadn't given any thought to.

"No, Disha, why do you say that? She is gonna get a better baby girl," I cooed.

"But she is already sick, and I know when people get old, they get sick, then sicker, then they die," she said, shrugging her shoulders.

I realized a lot of time had passed. I kept tryna plead my case to the little girl, but she would not listen. She just asked questions after questions.

"Come on, Disha, Grandma, is gonna be alright. Let's go see why they are taking so long there," I said, getting out of the passenger seat.

Disha let herself out of the backseat, jumping down from the 4x4 truck, and we walked to the front door together.

I heard someone yelling at the top of their lungs. Immediately, I panicked. It was a hell of a scream, and my pace quickened. As I approached the door, I heard a familiar voice.

"My mama is dead. Lord, no, she is dead," my auntie yelled as we stepped into the house.

She was sitting on the floor, reaching for the sky with both arms like she was trying to touch it. Tears fell from her face.

"Not my mama, don't tell me that. Mama! Maaammmaaaa!" she screamed.

Simon held her while she laid on the floor.

"Disha, go to the room with Lally and Em, I'll come to get you, OK?' I said to my baby sister.

She stood there staring at my aunt, cowering next to me while holding my leg.

"OK, Kahi," she replied, then motioned for me to bend down.

When I did, she whispered in my ear, "I told you."

She was observant, and sometimes it made me feel as if she was reincarnated. She was already putting together the pieces of the puzzle of life. Right then, I realized my sister was no slow leak.

Simon called my other aunts and uncles over. Auntie Ket-Ket sat on the couch with her eyes closed, telling Simon and the family that my mom didn't need to know right now because she wasn't in the condition to receive any news like this. She was too sick, and it would make her worse. This was a family secret that I wished they never kept. It was going to come back to bite them all in the ass.

My aunt Marie and her husband came down from Detroit a week before to visit Grandma Nah-Nah while she was in the hospital and my bed-ridden mother. Aunt Marie kept telling my mother she needed to go see a doctor, but my mother refused.

The whole family came through, including my cousins and some more people I hadn't seen in a while. Uncle Phil, Aunt Marie's husband, called us all to the front yard to say a prayer. Auntie Ket-Ket was whooping and hollering about Grandma's death. It was almost theatrical, but everybody ignored her outburst. She was always dramatic, so while she carried on, Uncle Phil just kept on praying.

"Lord Jesus, Father God, pleased bestow your mercy on your children, Father God."

As I listened to the prayer, I cried silently, eyes closed facing the sky. I was going to miss my Nah-Nah.

"Lord, you said it yourself, you would not burden your

children with more than we can bear. We lost our dear Nah-Nah Lord, but she's in your home now, Lord."

I was going to miss her smile, and her weird eyes, as my friend would say.

What nobody knew was that Grandma was the best secret holder. I had sex with Angelica in the living room one night, and Grandma Nah-Nah knew this and kept it to herself. I'll never forget the smile she gave me like she was proud of me before I walked out of the front door. She was sitting in a rocking chair on the far-left side of the porch. It surprised me because I thought she was in her room. When she saw the look on my face, she waved me off with her good arm and looked the other way. But before she turned her head, she playfully zipped her mouth shut with her fingers. Angelica never saw her. It was our secret. My secret was safe with her.

Another time I got hit by a car during a school day and had to limp back home. I knew I had fractured something, and my foot was super swollen. Grandma massaged my foot with special heating oil that she put over a fire. She boiled some grits, went outside, got two flat twigs, and tied the stick to my foot: one under my foot and the other across the top. She used both hands, the bad one had to hold my foot up, and the good one had to do what she knew best. Then she put the hot grits on my foot in plastic, and then covered the plastic with a towel. She repeated this every day for two weeks straight. I was back walking with a slight limp before my mother came home from her vacation to Haiti. I cried harder, thinking of all these memories.

"Please, Lord, watch over our beloved Nah-Nah and forgive her for her sins, Father God."

We all said, "Amen," in chorus.

I thought about how it was going to hurt my mother.

Opening my eyes, I looked around. My uncle Tony was crying hard, my Aunt Marie was crying, and so was everybody else.

It seemed as if we all had our moments to reflect on. Our own selfish memories eating away at our hearts.

"Love you, Nah-Nah," I mouthed silently into the deep gray sky.

The clouds seemed to form, and darkness overlooked us. I felt like the world had just lost someone special, and this was its way of showing me just how much.

I came home from school for my lunch break and saw my mother's car parked outside in its usual spot. She hadn't so much as crunk it up in a couple of weeks, and she still hadn't gotten out of bed. Nobody had told her about Grandma Nah-Nah yet. I hated the fact that I had to keep this secret from her for so long, and I couldn't question my elders. It seemed like anything I had to say didn't matter anyway.

Grandma Nah-Nah's funeral wasn't set until another two weeks. I wasn't trying to figure out how this was going to play out. No one had been home over the past week. Francia was out and about with Simon since he finally got a day off. Kadisha spent the week at Aunt Ket-Ket's house as usual. I spent a couple of days at Aunt Ket-Ket's house too. She needed me to run around with her to make funeral preparations.

While at the house, she sent me into her closet to look for some clothes she could drop off at the cleaners. She must have forgotten she had a half-ounce of weed sitting on top of some clothes on the shelf where she told me to look. I thought that was weird. How can this woman talk all that shit, yet she was slipping like that with weed in her closet in plain sight? I would have never known she smoked, had she not sent me into the closet, I wouldn't have figured out. I took a small bud and left the rest where I found it.

The house was cold when I walked in. The AC had been on full blast, yet outside was at least ninety degrees. I knew when I left, the AC was on seventy degrees. But when I checked, it was sixty degrees. Whoever fucked with it should have known it was too cold for my mom's condition.

When I walked into the room to check on my mother, she was balled up in a blanket like a baby. Her room was dark, and it smelled funny.

"Ma, you alright?" I asked, walking over to her.

The covers were cold, but underneath she was burning up. Her eyes were shut tight, but I could see she was moving them underneath her eyelids.

"Ma!" I said forcefully. "You ok?"

She still didn't open her eyes. She just shook her head, yes, shivering like she was cold. I could feel the heat coming from her body. I checked her forehead and throat with my hands like she had done when I was sick. She was burning up badly. Her body was sweaty and sticky.

"I think you need to go to the emergency room, Ma," I said, sitting down on the edge of the bed, stroking her hair.

She gestured no with her head. I knew it was her pride.

"All right then, let me clean you up. What's wrong, you can't get up to use the bathroom? I asked.

The stench coming from her bed was obviously fresh. I inspected the sheets around her carefully. She had pissed on herself. She wasn't saying anything, just shaking her head weakly. Her once full body was thinner, and the more I thought about it, the more I worried. I covered her back up and walked over to her bathroom. I ran her some warm water, putting body wash and bubble bath soap in the tub as it filled up. I walked back into the room, and she was still in the same position.

"Ma, I ran you a warm bath so I can clean all this stuff up, Ok?"

She didn't respond, just shook her head, yes.

When I helped her up, the smell began to settle in my nose. She had to do this when nobody was there. I wondered where Simon went and why the house was so cold, knowing she was sick and alone.

I helped her into the bathtub, but when it was time for her to stick her leg in the water, she shivered violently, I had to hold her, so she didn't fall in, taking me with her, shoes, and all!

After her legs went in, she calmed down a bit, slowly sinking into the water, putting her head back. I helped her out of her nightgown and underclothes while she was in the clean, warm water. Her face was saddened, and her bad health was evident to anybody who knew her.

Her jawline sucked in from the lack of food. She had stopped eating for the past two days and wasn't eating enough before that. She looked like she saw a ghost, and it scared the hell out of her. It was hurting me to see her like this, and I couldn't take it anymore. I told myself I had to do something about it. Then again, I thought about her stubbornness; whenever she said no, it was no. Nobody challenged that, but I was about to.

I left her in the tub to clean herself with a washcloth I handed her. I turned off the AC so the house would warm up. I went back into her room, took all the bedsheets off the bed, flipped the mattress over, and threw some clean sheets down. I needed someone to be there with me, but before I made the phone call, I had to check on her first.

I peeked my head in the bathroom. Seeing her in this condition was the worst state I had ever seen her. She was barely washing herself. While grabbing some clean clothes out of her drawer, I noticed a bible, some medicine, and a picture of the family that usually sat in the living room. Now the picture is sitting on the nightstand next to her bed. I gave her clothes.

"Hello, what's up, Grizz? Let me talk to Avia," I said, speaking to her cousin on the phone.

"Hey, I need you to come to the crib bae. Man, my old girl is looking really bad. She can't even talk, and she is burning up. I might need to call an ambulance, but I don't know if I should or not. Just come to the crib, so we can talk."

Avia agreed. She said her mom should be home in ten minutes and that she would be at my house in thirty minutes. It only took her twenty-five minutes to get to my house. That's one of the things I loved about her. She was all about me, and her loyalty couldn't be questioned. She made sure she showed me what loyalty was.

"Hey bae," she said.

She got out of the car and kissed me on the lips. I hate it when she does that in front of people, especially her mom. I wasn't one for public affection.

"What's good, Mrs. Smith, how are you doing?" I asked, waving at her mother from the passenger side window.

She waved back.

"I'm doing OK, son. Avia, what time do you want me to pick you up?"

"You can come late, Ma. I don't have school tomorrow, remember?"

"I'm coming to get you around nine, so be ready. OK,

Mahkahi, take care of my baby. I hope your mother gets better. Avia told me she was sick."

I hope she gets better too.

"She is a tough cookie, Mrs. Smith. We are gonna get her treated," I said, pointing from Avia to me.

"Ok, Doc. Avia, I'll be back, baby," her mom said, then left.

When we got back home, I brought Avia into the room to see my mother. She was back in the bed in the same position she was before. It was 5:00 p.m. Simon wasn't back yet, which I thought was odd.

"Ma, Avia is here to see you," I told her.

"Hi, mommy," Avia sang in her little girl's voice.

She reached over to kiss my mother's cheek.

"Kahi, she is burning up. She needs to go to the emergency room now. Don't you feel how cool it is here, and she is hot like this?

"Imma go get her something to drink, just sit here and keep her company."

"No, you get the water and the phone, and I'll get a towel for her forehead to cool her down. We have to call an ambulance."

I gave her a look, and she gave me one back like, go ahead. So, I obliged.

"This is 911, what is your emergency?" the operator said in a lazy tone.

"My name is Meg, I mean Mahkahi, and..."

"Your name is what, sir? And what is your emergency, sir?"

The operator asked, cutting me off."

"M.A.H.K.A.H.I. And my mother is very sick. Her body is hot, and she needs to see a doctor."

"Sir, did you say hot, sir. Did she get burned?"

"NO! She is sick, lady. You ain't heard nothing I said?" I have been here with her since the lunch period at eleven. When I got here, she was just in bed, and she has been like that for almost two weeks now. Her body wasn't burning up like it is now. I mean the temperature hot. With all due respect, we need an ambulance, please," I said, getting frustrated.

She was getting on my nerves with twenty-one questions.

"Calm down Kahi, what's wrong with you?" Avia said, walking over to the couch sitting next to me.

She put her hand on my back, calming me down.

"Nah, man. This lady is talking like a nigga is stupid, asking me all these stupid ass questions! All I need is an ambulance!" I said loud enough knowing, the operator could hear me.

I gave the phone to Avia. It wasn't really the operator's fault; I was speaking through the pain. Sending my mother to the hospital broke me down mentally. I never wanted to see her in a hospital unless it was for a check-up or if she was having her baby. My Grandma went to the hospital and never made it home. My emotions started getting the best of me.

"She said an ambulance is on the way, Mahkahi."

I just nodded. I wasn't even going there to face my mother. We sat in the living room quietly. All kinds of crazy thoughts ran through my head. I had to step up for my mom. I had to be the man of the house and do what I had to do until she got back.

I promised myself I wouldn't get in trouble. At least, not while she was gone, but even that proved to be difficult. I still had it in the back of my mind. I told myself one more lick, and that's it. I need to take the right path now.

LZ had another house for us that was supposed to be some guaranteed cash. He said it was only going to be him and me this time. I agreed, but that was before all this happened. But I needed the money and just couldn't turn down another opportunity. Besides, we went on a few licks and made some good money.

"One more lick," I kept telling myself. "Just one more, that's it. One more."

CHAPTER TWENTY-ONE

"**I**s your name Mahkahi?" the EMT asked as she made her way towards our house.

She was popping her chewing gum and making bubbles in my ear before the ambulance even pulled up. It seemed like I was having a bad dream and couldn't wake up. My mind was somewhere else.

"Where's Mrs. Guierra," the EMT asked.

I led them into the house, and when I opened the door, the EMT walked straight over to my mom, asking questions. A tear escaped my eyes. I knew that this was something she hated. She didn't like to be disobeyed, but I felt it would make her better on time, so she could attend Grandma's funeral.

As the EMT questioned her, she didn't say anything. I wished I could hear her voice. The strength of her voice would have made me stronger. But there was no sound, just a grunt, and a head nod.

He got on his walkie-talkie, and another EMT guy came into the room seconds later. He said some kind of code and shook his head. Disappointedly, it looked like a bad sign to me. The guy went back out to the ambulance and came in with a stretcher. Together they put her on it and rolled her out the front door. The whole neighborhood was on the block, being nosey.

I couldn't even think straight as the tears fell from my eyes. I watched her being tied down on the stretcher. Avia was on my shoulder the whole time, wiping my tears away with her thumb as they escaped my eyes. I felt like a sucker for crying in front of my girlfriend, but I couldn't help it. I couldn't imagine my mom not bouncing back from this shit. I needed her, I had promised her things, and if it killed me, so be it. I am going to keep my promises.

"Can I give my mom a kiss, sir?" I asked between hiccups and tears.

He was putting her in the back of the ambulance.

"Go ahead, son, but make it fast. I need you to sign some papers if you don't mind. Are you the only person here now?" the EMT guy asked.

"Alright, yeah. I don't even know where my stepdad is," I said honestly. "Did I just say stepdad?" I asked myself as I said it, then shook it off."

"Why didn't anyone call us sooner or bring her to see a doctor? She has a temperature of over a hundred. She's very, very sick," he said.

"I don't know," I said.

I really didn't know, but someone had to know she was getting worse. This shit was frustrating.

"Is she not going to make it or something?" As soon as those words escaped my mouth, I cried harder.

"No, no. I'm not saying that. I've seen people go to the hospital in worse condition than she is in and make it. We have to see what's wrong with her first. Don't jump to any conclusions. Your mom is going to be okay. They'll take care of her."

They had the back door opened. The guy was doing something to her, putting things in her arms, from her to a machine. He stuck a mask over her face that was hooked up to something like a pump. It went up and down as her chest heaved.

Tears wouldn't stop rolling down my face. Her mouth

had to stay open as he pushed a tube in her throat and another in her nose. Needles were in her arms. She left her head slumped to one side like she was defeated. She was motionless like she would never be able to walk again. This moment alone made me appreciate what I had. Even with Avia there, I was still broken. I had to be strong, though. I just kept wishing this wasn't real.

As the day went by, the sun started to settle. I took a moment looking at her face, her ashy lips. My tears fell on her arm as I grabbed her hand.

"We have to get going, little man," one of the EMTs said.

I ignored him.

I felt her hand move towards mine. I held on as tight as I could. She tried again and again to grip my hand, but her strength wasn't there.

"Ma, I feel you," I said, wiping the tears from my face with my sleeve.

"Ma, you are going to be okay. He said they are taking you to Waypark Regional, and as soon as Simon is back, we're coming to see you."

She tried to squeeze my hand again, only making it move slightly.

"Imma go now, ma because they have to take you, OK?" I said, through tears and snot running out of my nose.

Her mouth moved a little bit.

"What, Ma?" I asked, putting my ear to her mouth.

Her breath was hot, and I felt the word love float into my ear.

The last thing I remember was the ambulance whisking her away. I stood in the street feeling alone in a world only my mind could explain. There was only one word to describe how I felt—dark.

People watched me cry on bended knees, Avia covering my body with her warmth.

• • •

"Imma hit the back streets, soon as we see the bridge, we are jumping out!" I yelled over the sirens.

The speedometer on the dashboard read 100 mph, but the car was only doing thirty. The police car was gaining speed, almost touching the bumper.

"Damn, this pussy-ass Saturn is slower than a mother-fucker. What made you get this slow-ass shit?"

LZ wasn't paying me any attention in the passenger seat as I screamed at him. He was turned all the way around like he was trying to take a mental picture. My foot was all the way down on the gas pedal, and no matter what I did, I couldn't shake this motherfucker. The cop car stayed right on my ass.

• • •

Earlier that morning, I caught the bus to the 163rd street mall to meet up with LZ, who was waiting for me when I got there. He had his tools, and I had mine. He made sure to file down the key the night before so we wouldn't waste time looking for a car. I brought a book bag with the B&E kit too. There were different size screwdrivers, a mini crow-bar, and some gloves. It all went as planned until we came out of the house to a white lady jogging by, damn near fall-ing over her own feet. Her mouth was wide open, breaking her neck to look at us. She must have known the Jews who lived in the house.

LZ screamed at her, "Get away from here, bitch before I kill you!"

"Just couldn't help it, huh? Had to do some cornball-ass shit," I said when the lady took off running faster.

"Let me guess, you think she would've thought two young niggas in a Jewish area, with black gloves and bags in their hands, we're just here to visit! Fuck you talking about it? Come on, let's get in the whip, fool," he said.

He was right, we had to get the fuck away from there. But he's wrong for the intimidation he just put down. This probably made her want to call the police quicker if she didn't already have intentions.

We went back in and got the rest of the shit we left behind. A small safe we couldn't get open and some speakers for a stereo system. We pulled out the driveway and drove two blocks, and that's when we stopped at a 3-way stop sign. I flashed the lights for the police car on our right, but he didn't move. He put on his lights.

Over the loudspeaker, he said, "Driver of the black car, do not move, I repeat, do not move."

That's when I took off at full speed. And that's how we ended up in a full-blown car chase with police.

I hit a few blocks, running stop signs, and avoiding other cars, but the police car was like milk on cereal. I couldn't shake this cracker for nothing. I watched LZ in the passenger seat watching the cop. Me being the rookie driver I was, I forgot to use the rearview mirror and ended up turning my whole body around to see how close he was. I was making a sharp left and had already started it. When I turned my body to see where the police were, my hand shifted the car slightly right, and by the time I turned back around to straighten the car out, it was too late. BAAM! We smashed into a palm tree.

● ● ●

Daylight slowly crept through my eyelids. It felt like I was splashed with juice. My face felt wet. I thought I was wiping the juice off, but when I looked at my hands, blood covered my fingers. I tried to wiggle out of the wedge I was in. The only thing I kept thinking about was my mama and that money. I couldn't go to jail while my mom was still in the hospital, sick as hell.

Smoke started coming in through the vents and was taking over the car slowly. Over to my right, LZ was leaning back, passed out. His head had a hole in it that gave it a look like the inside of some pregnant pussy: pink with blood coming out of it. Both of us had head injuries.

"LZ, get up my nigga, I think the car catching on fire! LZ, get up!" I yelled, starting to panic.

I freed my legs, reaching over and shaking him at the same time. He stirred a little, then opened his eyes.

"Where am I?" He looked confused.

"We gotta get out of this fucking car. I know where we gonna be if we don't. Shake ya head nigga, we have to go now," I exclaimed.

He reached in the back seat, moving quickly. He tried using his shirt to wipe the blood from the hole in his head, but the blood just kept coming out.

"How long was I out? Damn my head hurt, kid!" he said, leaning forward, closing his eyes, and putting on his book bag at the same time.

"Not long, it's probably been like a second or so. Are you ready? Let's go!"

With that, I got out of the driver's side. LZ was having a hard time opening his door, so he climbed out of the driver's side behind me.

"FREEZE! Get down, with your hands up, you

little shit!" I heard the officer say, but I didn't pay him any attention.

I could tell he was at a safe distance, too far away to grab hold of me, so I helped LZ out of the car.

"Stop now. Get on the ground, or I'll be forced to shoot!" he yelled again.

This time it was a little shaky.

The bridge was less than ten feet away. All we had to do was get across it. And I was getting away by any means. I looked at the officer, then at the car. I saw the damage done. We ended up avoiding the lake by hitting the palm tree. We could have died either way. The car was totaled. The whole front end was smashed up to the dashboard, and the windows were stuck closed. If we ended up in the water, we probably would have drowned. I had to think fast. He was either a super cop, which I doubted, or a scary one.

"Oh, shit!" I yelled.

Using the oldest trick in the book, the cop retreated and cowered down behind his driver's side door, with a gun pointed at us. By the bright blue shirt, he was wearing, he was still a rookie.

Halfway across the bridge, LZ said, "My head hurts Megaman, go head bra, I'll thug it out. I can't run no more."

As LZ talked, blood kept pouring down his face. The adrenaline was making him bleed more. My cut was dried-up, but the knot on my head could have been seen by Stevie Wonder.

"Come on nigga, pull ya motherfucking shirt down, yo. We looking at a lot of time, and my old girl is in the hospital. I will be damned if we go to jail. Ain't none of us going to jail today!" I said, pulling off one of the two shirts I had on, tying it around his head.

I pulled on his arm, and we took off running.

We cut through the V like some vets. Still, because of the police perimeter, we had to run in the back of the V where all the residential areas were, in the same area Monte' told me to stay away from. But like I said, rules are meant to be broken.

Jumping fence after fence, the worst of our troubles had just begun. The helicopter swooped above us.

"Damn my nigga, they are acting like we killed someone, fool. They brought the birds out!" LZ said, looking up at the copter.

"Keep running, fuck that bird," I instructed.

LZ was slowing us up, complaining that his head was hurting. The blood came through the shirt. I guess it was more serious than I thought. But I wasn't going to jail, I didn't give a fuck.

We ended up in a bush as the helicopter flew over our heads in circles.

"Just wait till it goes past us and make a U-turn. When it goes past us, we go through that door, wipe your face, you got blood everywhere. And make sure that blood doesn't drip on the floor because they might bring dogs. If they smell it, they are gonna know where we are at," I instructed.

"How the fuck do you know all this, nigga? You act like you did this before," LZ said, wiping his face.

"Plenty of times, but not with the bird. The other shit about blood, nigga you don't watch no movies? The dogs always follow the scent," I said, shaking my head, thinking, this nigga needs to get back in the game.

We were facing serious jail time, and I had too much going on to be in jail.

After jumping a tall ass fence, we ended up in someone's

backyard. Out of nowhere, a little pig ran past us going crazy. I don't know where it came from, but it scared the shit out of me. We ran toward the door that was left slightly open.

"Who's there?" asked a lady whose voice sounded like someone with a bad smoking habit.

No sooner did she ask, she coughed miserably back to back.

"Bobby, Grandma," I yelled in my best little white boy voice, taking a chance.

LZ gave me a 'yeah right' look.

"Come on in, Bobby," she said.

LZ gave me another look.

I just shrugged my shoulders. We walked through the house. It smelled terrible. I almost gagged from the nasty taste in my throat. This house was like a little petting zoo. Birdcages and mouse cages were lined up everywhere. A snake cage sat in the kitchen where we came in.

Soon as LZ saw her with her back turned, he moved in quickly, putting his hands around her mouth with his bloody hands, whispering something in her ear. She tried to fight for a second, but when he turned her around, and she saw me, she stopped moving. Tears fell from her eyes. She was easy to handle, a small little lady with a cane. She didn't put up much of a fight. He held her while I checked the whole house. The house was filthy. If I had a guess, I'd say she lived alone.

"Yo, ain't nobody in the crib, fool," I said to LZ, holding my nose shut. "You stay by yourself, old lady?" I asked her after I walked around.

She shook her head, yes. I believed her. This old lady was living in a cluster of stank, shit, and junk. She was a habitual hoarder.

"Look, ma'am, we don't want to hurt you. My partner here and I just need to buy some time. That's it. If you just chill out, we'll leave. I'm going to tell him to let you go, but if you scream, he'll hurt you. He's not in a good mood, as you can see. We're having a very bad day, OK?"

She nodded. By this time, she had stopped crying. I felt sorry for the old lady. She was helpless, but we were desperate. We had to put the stress on her just in case she tried anything.

I heard the helicopter fly by a few times, then heard it in the distance. I doubt they knew where we were because they would have been at this house.

"You should have said that the first-time young man. Why would you scare an old woman like me like that?" she asked, shocking us.

We just looked at each other, surprised. "Ya'll don't have to worry about my rating on none of you. My time on this earth is short, and I won't spend another day on it, making other people's lives harder than it probably already is," she continued. "What did you guys do if you don't mind me asking? Kill somebody?" she whispered, looking around as if someone else would hear her.

"Nah, we ain't kill nothing, but they acting like we did," LZ told her.

"Ok, if you say so. I'll sit right here till you get it done, so help yourself," she said. "By the way, my name is Mary Lou, not an old lady. Don't like that name," she stated, rolling her eyes. Then she went to sit on the couch.

"Where's the towel old la--, I mean, Mary Lou?" LZ asked, looking at me quizzically.

"I'll show you, really need to clean that cut up son, looks really nasty. You could catch something really easy with an open wound."

I was thinking the same thing about LZ's blood-smeared face.

"I got some bandages and a first aid kit. I was a nurse for thirty-three years, I'm retired now. Follow me, son," she said, while LZ followed her down the hall.

I sat down on the old dusty couch, trying to gather my thoughts. I turned on the old TV to watch the news, and we had made it to the big screen.

'Two unidentified suspects wanted in connection with a burglary early this morning on the corner of 167Th street and 13th avenue. Officer Bellachik, seen over there, said the two suspects tried to ram his patrol car. He avoided them by swerving out of harm's way. He then pursued the suspects in a high-speed chase that ended with the suspect's stolen vehicle slamming into that palm tree over there. Officer Bellachik said the suspects jumped out of the car enraged, pointing an object at him. He ran for cover when he hurt himself on the car door. The suspects escaped on foot. Dogs have been at the scene working to find them, but they seemed to disappear in thin air. A witness, a woman out for her morning jog, said that one of the suspects threatened to kill her.'

I started laughing so hard that I was choking. That shit was too funny. They piled lies on top of lies; hell, it was their word against ours.

Real don't reside nowhere, not even in law enforcement, I thought to myself.

'Please call Crime Stoppers with any information leading to their arrests. This is Kate Hernandez with Channel Seven News. Back to you, John.'

CHAPTER TWENTY-TWO

We had two days before Grandma Nah-Nah's funeral. I hadn't even gotten a chance to get a suit yet. Uncle Phil had been so busy taking care of the funeral arrangements and checking up on my mother at the hospital, that he hadn't had time to take me shopping for the suit like he promised. After the prayer session the night Grandma Nah-Nah passed, everybody but the small children went to see Nah-Nah at the hospital.

I was numb, staring at my Nah-Nah lying in that hospital bed. The only memories of her now were the present ones that stained my memories. She was lying there dead, with her eyes closed, face-up, hands at her sides. There were no tubes nor monitors hooked up to her body, reading her vitals. The blood had stopped flowing through her body, giving her the look of a mannequin. Someone went so far as to brush her curly hair back. Her long hair went past her shoulder, coming out by her underarms and down past her chest.

When I first walked into the room, doctors were scrambling around, trying to make room for our little family. The air smelled like medicine. It seemed like when I walked in, being the youngest there, all eyes were on me. I looked on from a distance. I turned back around and walked out the door, soon as my Aunt Ket-Ket walked in with her drama.

"Come back in, Kahi, say goodbye to Nah-Nah," Aunt Marie said.

I did as she asked and came back into the room. I sat next to Aunt Marie as she put her arm around my shoulder.

Her breath smelled of fresh gum. Her cheeks and nose were bright red from crying. Her free hand held out a tissue, while I observed the lost look on her face. I held eye contact with her.

"I can't, Auntie. I don't wanna see Nah-Nah like that. Just let me vibe out here," I said, leaning back against her arm.

It was comforting to feel her warm touch. My aunt wasn't the judgmental type, neither was my uncle. She didn't agree with what I was doing, but she never questioned me about anything. Instead, she just gave me sound advice and minded her business. In the back of my mind, all I thought about was my mother, lying in a hospital bed, clueless. I had my emotions riding on my back.

"I know, baby, this must be hard for you because it's hard for me. It's alright, death is part of life. But you know Nah-Nah is in a better place."

Tears welled up in her eyes as she zoned out, then she continued. "We all know Nah-Nah would want us closer to her instead of out here. I'm not going to push you but think about coming to say goodbye to your Grandma. You know I love you, right?" she added.

"Yeah, I know you love me. But that doesn't mean God won't take you from me. He took my daddy from me. He made my mom sick. He did all these things, and it doesn't matter about love, Auntie. God still does what he wants to do," I said, staring into her soul.

My body ached, and I was so mad. It felt like every fiber in my bones agreed with what I had to say. I meant every word at that moment. I was tired of going through this. I was only 14 years old, and I had seen more people die in the hood than on TV. This death was too close to home.

"God wills what he wants, nephew. Don't blame this on God. This is the way life works. Bad things happen to good people, bad things happen to bad people, good things happen to bad people. The point is, He tests your strength. Just like He can give you life, he can take it away. Not because He is being mean, but He has a purpose for you," she said, getting up.

My Auntie was only five-feet tall, but she over stood the highest of mountains. She was the definition of strong, though the worry showed on her face. I had no doubt she would get through this.

"Thank you, Auntie. I'll be there in a minute."

"Thank me for what?" She asked. "I'm your family, we stick together. Now don't sit out there forever because we gotta get going in a few minutes," she said seriously.

When I walked into the room, it was like when Moses parted the Red Sea. Everybody on the left side stepped back, and everybody on the right side stepped back. I kept my eyes straight, staring at the bottom of Grandma's feet, which were pointed straight in the air. She had on thick baby blue socks with little white dots on them, and a white hospital gown that flowed all the way down to near her ankles. Her whole body looked bloated. I didn't notice right away, but the closer I got, the more visible it became. I stared at my Nah-Nah's face. She is dark now. The last time I saw her, she was damn near pale, like a white woman.

"It's OK," someone said.

"Go ahead," I heard someone else say when I took a moment to collect myself.

I didn't know what to go ahead and do. I just stared for a while, standing over her. Then my body just reacted without me thinking. I hugged my Grandma, my face buried into her chest like I've done so many times before. My arms wrapped loosely around her body. I cried softly on her chest, listening, waiting, but instead, silence overwhelmed me. There was no heartbeat, only heartache. The silence in the room was broken by people crying. I could hear it where I rested like an echo. Nobody touched me, they just left me there glued to her body.

I heard a faint humming that caused me to lift my head up. Uncle Phil's soft voice broke into a mumble. Slowly, I could hear the words.

"The storm is over. The storm is over now..." He sang his favorite song.

• • •

I sat in the living room, staring at my reflection in the mirror. Across the top part of my chest, I got 'Hell-uva-life' tattooed just days before. I had Uno take me to the tattoo shop he went to around the way called Dogg-Town. This was my first tattoo, and it hurt like hell. Kenny, the tattoo man, wasn't light handed either. It was painful going in and going out. When he was finished, I was satisfied. I truly was living a helluva life. My Grandma Nah-Nah had just passed away, and my mother had gone to the hospital not too long before that. Not only that, but I was trying to duck jail, all in the same breath.

Thanks to me, the mirrors were extra clean. I took the time out to clean the whole house myself since no one else was home to do it. I knew my mother would have had a fit if she came home to the mess we made over the last couple of weeks. Tired from cleaning, I dialed up Avia's room phone. She had a separate line from her house. It was going on two in the morning, and I was hoping she was up.

"Hello," I said, smiling, thinking of the real reason I called her.

Avia was trying to dodge the question I asked her. We were going back and forth about me being her first. She had every right to be the way she was because, in reality, I was a dog. I couldn't help it, though. I was young, dumb, and full of cum. What's a dog to do when they throwing the dog a bone? Eat it!

"Mahkahi, what time is it, and don't we have a funeral to go to in the morning?" she said through her sleep.

That morning was Grandma Nah-Nah's funeral, and Avia had invited herself. I guess she wanted to be some kind of moral support. She had a heart like that. That's probably why I always kept a special place in my heart for her.

"Don't worry about that, I got that. My uncle gotta bring me my suit, so he is gonna be the one to wake me. Besides, the funeral ain't till nine anyway. But you still ain't answer my question from earlier," I said, smiling on the other end. I knew this would embarrass her a little.

"I just know you ain't call me…hold up! At two-something in the morning to talk about that. You know Lisa and I are going to the funeral too, and I need my sleep, Mahkahi. Why are you up so damn late, boy?" she questioned, frustrated.

"I had to clean the whole house by myself because nobody else would. Simon been at work, back and forth with my uncle to the hospital, and making funeral arrangements."

"You are a mess. How is your little tattoo on that bird chest healing? You cleaning it like the man told you to?" she asked, snickering.

"Little chest, huh? So, you got jokes? You know they say big things come in small packages."

We both started laughing.

"I have been cleaning it up, though, making sure it's healing well," I assured her.

"You heard from your mama yet? How ain't nobody tell her nothing, Mahkahi, and she is still in the hospital? Somebody needs to tell that lady. Tomorrow her mother is getting buried," she said seriously.

The last time I saw my mom was when LZ and I took the public bus to visit her at the hospital. She went from doing alright to back to the breathing machine. I had to call the head nurse into the room during our visit. She was talking in short breaths. Every time I asked her why she was talking like that, she would tell me she didn't know why and would point to her chest. I thought I heard them tell Simon she looked to be getting better, only to find out otherwise.

That same day, I spoke to the head nurse, who said they had to have a doctor take a look at her. They rushed her to the intensive care unit (ICU). The doctor told me she had Pneumonia, and that there wasn't much they could do but feed her medicine and watch the body heal itself.

"I ain't heard nothing since she went to ICU, but why are you tryna dodge the question still A.v.i.a, I said jokingly, breaking down her name.

I really didn't want to talk about my mom. I was going through enough.

"OK, Megastar, maybe," she said jokingly.

"It's Mr. Megaman, and what do you mean? Maybe what?"

"I said maybe, maybe is maybe. I don't know. I don't really want to talk about that." She sighed, frustrated.

Avia was very shy when it came to talking about sex. I tried to be patient with her, though I was not faithful. I wanted what we were missing. I was getting tired of having a girlfriend, and all she wanted to do was dry-bone and kiss. That shit got boring. I ain't have time for the games.

'CLICK, CLICK, CLICK'

"That's someone on your line, Mahkahi. That better not be no bitch calling you this damn late," she said, with an attitude.

I was hoping it wasn't either. I knew if my mother was here, she would be doing a lot of cursing if someone called her home about me this late at night.

"You feisty little devil, calm down, young wippa snappa. It's probably the wrong number. Hold up ugly, let me see who it is," I said, clicking over.

"Hello, who is this?" I said, impatiently.

"Waypark Regional Medical Center. May I ask with whom I am speaking?" The man asked.

"This Mahkahi, what's up?"

"I need to speak to Mr. Wright," he said, referring to Simon.

"For what? He is asleep. Do you have a message or something?" I asked.

My mouth got dry, and my heart started to race. Where I sat, the hot air hit me like a ton of bricks. I couldn't figure out why I felt so weak, so faint, so quickly.

"Well, sir, I'm Doctor Echols, Ms. Guierra's doctor. Tell Mr. Wright, that I am sorry to inform him that the patient, Ms. Guierra, has expired."

"What the fuck you mean expired?" I screamed loudly.

Everybody in the house was asleep. I was thinking and wanted to believe this motherfucker called at three in the morning when people were sleeping to talk about expired medicines. He could have called about this in the morning when people ate breakfast, not at three in the morning.

'CLICK'

Avia hung up on the other line. Now I am getting mad. She probably thought it was a bitch on the other line for real. The thought of it made me really mad. Now she was on the other line calling back, probably to curse me out.

"What do you mean expired?" I asked the doctor.

He was quiet.

"Sir, Ms. Guierra is gone. I'm sorry, but someone has to come to claim her body. I'm sorry," he said again. "I'm sorry" was all he kept saying.

Sorry for what? What the fuck was he sorry for?

You can't be fucking calling my house to tell me my mother was dead.

All I could remember was watching the mirror shatter into a zillion pieces and burying my head into the couch. My body began to shake, my eyes taking in nothing in particular. Everything around me became blurry, black as if someone put a shield over my face. I couldn't understand what I was going through. I didn't want to believe this to be true. "

How is he gon play like that?

When I finally came back to reality, Simon was right there looking at me like I was crazy. When he saw the tears in my eyes and the broken mirror on the floor, he took a knee and began to cry himself. Through all the ruckus, Kadisha, and Francia didn't stir, they were sound asleep.

As hard as I threw that phone, I was surprised when it rang. It had broken glass all over it. It took everything in my power to pick it up. My soul was torn. Now wasn't the time. The way I was feeling, I would kill to get my point across. Don't fuck with me!

"Don't play with me, Mahkahi. You left me on the line to talk to that bitch. Don't try me like that," Avia ranted.

I didn't say anything immediately. I watched Simon walk out the front door with a cigarette in one hand and his cell phone in the other.

"Hello, boy. I know you hear me talking to you."

I blinked, and a tear fell off my face.

I couldn't stop them from coming down. It felt like second nature. I had to let the words flow casually so I wouldn't break down.

"I wasn't on the phone with no bitch, Avia," I said calmly.

"Why do you sound like you guilty, Mahkahi? Who were you on the phone with?" she asked, with an attitude.

I could tell she was snaking her neck on the other end. I know her like the back of my hand. There was a small pause.

"She is gone Avia, she is gone, man!" I cried into the receiver.

"What do you mean? Oh my God, Kahi! Stop playing," she yelled, then went down to a whisper. "Kahi, are you serious? Oh, my God, I'm so sorry."

She asked me if I was serious. I don't know, was I? I still didn't believe it. Who knew my whole world would come crashing down on me like this?

"Imma call you back." As my hand found its way to the red button, I heard her say 'sorry' like I ain't already heard that. Everybody was sorry but for me. I wanted to feel numb. I didn't care. I was too mad to care about anybody saying sorry. Fuck Sorry.

I walked to the front door, half confused and weak. I sat next to Simon, who was leaning on the truck with his phone in one hand and a fresh cigarette in the other. He was having a serious conversation with someone. He caught me off guard, handing me a cigarette with a lighter. Throughout the exchange, there were no words. My initiation to manhood, I thought. He was letting me know I wasn't alone, but I'm a man now. I put the cigarette in my pocket and replaced it with a half of a joint of some Arizona I had in my pocket. I planned on smoking it after I got off the phone with Avia.

I sucked on that Arizona joint like she was all I had, and let the smoke fill my lungs. Paralysis settled in from the potency of the weed. In other words, I was as high as fuck! Silence thickened the air after Simon got off the phone, and I just stared out in the distance.

The only way to describe it was that the full moon lit the sky up like a natural flashlight. Between Simon and I, the only other noises the world allowed my ears to hear was the sound of dogs whining in the distance, neighbored by crickets rubbing their wings together, singing nature's annoying songs.

● ● ●

I had to stop talking for a minute. I leaned back in my chair, staring up at the white ceiling. Some of what was said got me in my feelings and was tryna make me weak. The man in me wouldn't allow it to happen. I was hurt, I can't deny that, but over the years I had become numb.

"Ms. Calder, are you alright? I asked, adjusting my shirt.

"Oh, my God! Mahkahi," she said through teary eyes.

I noticed right away she was no longer in character. She addressed me by my first name.

"This is... I can't... I mean the morning of your grandmother's funeral, your mom...This is something I don't think anyone in their right mind would have been able to handle," Ms. Calder said.

She produced a tissue and dabbed the corner of my eyes.

"I'm sorry, I'm getting really emotional," she said. "I've heard stories before, but damn this shit touches me a little differently. She said, shaking her head. I'm so out of character," she said finally.

She looked around the room, trying to avoid eye contact with me.

She probably didn't realize it, but this wasn't her fault, and I had to let her know why.

"Characters are movies. Actors read from scripts, but feelings are real. One thing you got to realize Ms. Calder is that there's a difference. You're human, and humans have emotions," I said, then continued. "Back then, I couldn't even talk to someone about this without my feelings getting involved. It crushed me from the inside out," I said, pointing to my heart, then shrugged my shoulders.

"I could only imagine what you must have felt. I didn't mean it like that. I hope you do understand," she said sincerely, then she went quiet.

Her face was beet red, and the pain she was feeling was evident from the way she spoke and acted. Every now and then, she would look at me shaking her head like this was unbelievable. I wished plenty of times that I woke up from this bad dream, only to realize this was my life. I guessed she noticed the tears she shed that fell on some of her papers. She dabbed the papers with her tissue, trying to clean up the mess.

"Let me tell you about this crazy thing that happened to me," I said, trying to break the thick ice that settled in between us.

There was an eerie silence, and I could tell she wasn't really ready to get out of her feelings. Regardless of the facts, the story must go on.

"You are a very special person, Mr. Guierra," she said suddenly. I can't believe you're so strong," she said, staring.

As much as I wanted to believe it, I let it flow in one ear and out the other.

"I just wanted to let you know that," she continued, looking at her watch.

Naturally, I looked up at the clock on the wall. I still had thirty minutes until I hit the yard.

"We only have thirty minutes, we have to shut it down," she said disappointedly.

I had thirty minutes. I thought at least I'd get through most of where I really wanted the story to end.

Then I continued...

CHAPTER TWENTY-THREE

"Kahi, Kahi, Kahi."

"Huh? Who is that?"

"Wake up Kahi, I need to talk to you."

I got up, sitting on my bed, rubbing the cold out of my eyes. I felt like there was a big cloud over my head. I kept thinking about sleeping, and just wished I could get back to it. I listened for the voice—my mother's.

Suddenly, she appeared before me, dressed in her pretty white suit. Her face was a big blur, but as I imagined her beauty. As always, she was the brightest of the stars.

"Mama," I whispered, needing to hear her voice.

I squinted my eyes, trying to focus on her face, but my eyes wouldn't let me.

I was able to see a glimpse of her here and there. When I looked around my room, anxiety hit me. *This isn't right.* Her voice called my racing heart. When she reached out for me, there was an invisible wall between us. I couldn't understand why when she reached for me, there was an unimaginable distance between us. When I reached back, it was the same. I just wanted to feel her hands like I used to.

"Kahi, you and your sisters are all you have now. Remember what I told you?" she asked, blinding me with her beauty. I tried to stare straight in her face but was losing focus.

"Of course, I remember," I responded.

"Make sure you treat your sisters like you treat your mother, with respect, and like a queen," we said in unison.

A pain shot through my arm, and my vision started to get blurry.

"Ma, what happened? Why can't I see you? Move from the light, Ma," I said, struggling to look directly at her, I tried to follow the sweet sound of her voice.

"I miss you like crazy," I said.

Something felt off in my head, like a puzzle, but I couldn't figure it out. It felt something like defeat, or maybe it was closure.

"I know, son, I know. Just remember," she said, smiling, her teeth made the light around her shine brighter. "I'm always with you."

Her voice started to fade. She reached out again, but her reach was distant. It broke my heart, and I couldn't handle what I was feeling.

"Ma, let me come with you, where are you going?' I reasoned when she turned to leave.

Her whole back was visible, her long hair above her shoulders in a huge bun, just the way she likes it.

I felt a hand on my shoulder, someone mumbling in the background.

"Kahi, Kahi, Kahi."

"Huh?" I answered, jumping up, looking around my room.

I looked past the door where my mother disappeared, but she wasn't there. Just voices talking. I looked back at the clock on my nightstand, and it was 5:30 am.

"How did I get to bed?" I mumbled to myself.

When I looked down at the pants I remembered having on, my memory slowly came back to me. I was shirtless, looking down at the tattoo on my chest. I put both hands on my head, realizing why it hurt so badly. Tears welled up in my eyes. I thought this moment I was experiencing was just a dream. It wasn't. It was real.

"I'm here, baby," I heard my Aunt Marie say.

I looked past her, stuck in my thoughts. Her hand on my shoulder, the same warmth I felt before.

"Everything is going to be alright, baby, come here," she said, pulling me into a tight embrace. My eyes were wide open, looking around the room, hoping my mother would somehow pop out in the corner, but we were the only two in the room. Tears welled up in my eyes again. I listened to the voices in the hallway.

"We have to tell the pastor what happened first," said Uncle Phil. "Then we can tell people. Simon, we can't just drop this on everybody before we lay Nah-Nah to rest. It's too much as it is. Can you imagine? Ket-Ket called me this morning, and she was still crying, man. I have to go over there now, and I don't know how imma deal with this woman."

Uncle Phil stood in the hallway trying to be discreet, speaking low, but not low enough.

"Sweetheart, Mahkahi awake yet? Uncle Phil asked from the hallway.

"Yeah, baby, he is awake," Aunt Marie said, looking at me with soft eyes.

Then she got up off the bed. "Kahi, let me talk to your Uncle Phil. We have to bring Kadisha to Ket-Ket to get ready for Nah-Nah's funeral. The Lord have mercy on her soul. I don't know where to start, baby. I need you to be strong for Auntie, ok?" she said, putting her hand on the door looking back at me.

I just shook my head in understanding. Strong wasn't a force I was ready to stand up against. Not right now, anyway. I was too fragile at heart and mind, like a newborn baby all over again. She walked out of the room, pulling the door closed.

My throat was so dry that it hurt when I tried to swallow. I could still taste the joint I'd been smoking on my breath. I ended up rolling another joint after I finished the one, I had in my back pocket. Simon and I sat outside the whole night and never said two words to each other. We just sat there in silence, and that's all I could remember. All of a sudden, my head started to ache, forcing me to lie back.

"Fucking weed hangover," I mumbled, rubbing my temples with both my index fingers. Then my door swung back open, causing me to sit straight up.

"What's up, nephew?" Uncle Phil said, coming through the door.

He sat at the foot of the bed. His eyes were blood-shot red like he hadn't slept in days. I laid all the way back, both arms behind my head. I was thinking, I hope this nigga doesn't come here to preach. I wasn't in the mood for no God-talk. Too much was going on. My mind was in a world of shit. I wanted to cry out. I didn't know how to cry no more. The only pain was my broken heart and this headache. The disbelief was visible on both our faces.

"There's this saying that goes, no matter how bad your circumstances, as long as your heart is still pumping and you got all your limbs, you keep pushing," His arm pumping forward in a thrust. Tears streamed down his face.

I was so fed up with talking, I just looked at the ceiling. That shield over my heart had turned rock solid. Hate covered it. They told me she might get better. They kept telling me that everything was going to be OK. 'Just pray,' my aunt, Marie, told me that day we all prayed together. 'Put it in God's hands.' When it was all said and done, God ain't do nothing. He caused me pain and resentment towards the people that lied about life being alright. Everybody to me from this point on were liars.

"I'm hurting too, Kahi, and I know you are mad as hell right now. I just lost my mother-in-law and sister-in-law. I loved them with open arms, Kahi. Buddy, you just have to keep pushing, if not for yourself, then for the family," he said, wiping his tears.

I just stared, wanting to let him know I heard this same shit before, just in a different way.

"I'll go get your stuff out of the car, buddy, you don't have to say anything right now," he said. Then he continued, "Later we have to talk. I'll come back and pick you up unless you want to ride with me to the funeral. I'm going alone in my car. I can't be in that limo with your Aunt Ket-Ket acting all crazy."

He was right. I wasn't trying to ride with her either. And they were going to break the news to her. No way in hell I was riding with them.

"Just come get me," was all I uttered. He walked over to me and hugged me like his wife had just done. I hugged him back. When he walked out the door, I picked myself up off the bed, put all my stuff together, and went to take my shower. When I got out of the shower, I had a grey suit, with a white dress shirt, black tie, and shiny black shoes laid at the foot of my bed. A little note was on top of my suit.

> *Be back in an hour to get you. Avia said some friends named LZ, Ace, and Monte' were riding with her If you don't mind. I took the liberty to tell her it was OK (smile). And Kahi, please try and stay sober with respect for your Nah-Nah. I love you,*
> *—Uncle Phil.*

I cried again. I couldn't believe I had to a funeral today. I put the note down and got dressed. I put on my tie, which I learned how to put on when I was at Jann Mann. They had a program called Five thousand role models that they forced me to enter. They taught boys how to be men. Doing shit like learning to tie a tie. I picked it up quickly. I checked myself out in the mirror, wiping my tears away.

My hair was still tight. I cut it into a Caesar, bald on the sides, and low at the top. I brushed it like Monte' taught me, laid it down like he taught me, and my waves were spinning in thick rows above my head.

I caught a reflection of a family picture I kept on my dresser and picked it up. The picture was of me, Nah-Nah, my mother, who was pregnant with Francia, and Kadisha. Ma was big as hell from her pregnancy, standing at Bayfront Park in downtown Miami. One night, she told us to get dressed and stroll out. There were strips among strips of stores. Bayfront is mainly a tourist attraction. I stared at the picture through the mirror while adjusting the tie once more. I went over to the dresser. The clock read 7:00 a.m. I picked the picture up off the dresser. I closed my eyes, mentally preparing myself for what was to come.

CHAPTER TWENTY-FOUR

"**L**adies and gentlemen, we are gathered here today to celebrate the glorious life of Mrs. Neliah Marie Baptiste. To her friends and family, she preferred Grandma Nah-Nah or just Nah-Nah.

"I want to share a quick story with you all before beginning the service. I can remember when I first met this amazing woman. She was not ashamed of her title as Grandma Nah-Nah. As a matter of fact, she wore the title proudly. With all due respect, I would like to address this great woman as such.

"Grandma Nah-Nah was a good woman, a God-fearing woman. Grandma Nah-Nah was the type of woman that would go out of her way to help a neighbor, a friend, her family, or even a stranger if they needed help. When I first met her, she introduced herself as Grandma Nah-Nah, and out of the blue, she gave me a coconut cake. We had just met, but still, she was so respectful and kind that she just had to do her good deed. Lord knows that cake was some of the best Haitian cake I've ever had. Bless her soul!

"I would see this woman act as a mentor to the troubled kids in the neighborhood, no one would say anything if she intervened because they knew Grandma Nah-Nah always had their best interest at heart.

"I learned that every parent who went to this church respected her every decision. It pains me to say that our church and our community has truly lost an angel. I would like to say to the family that your loved one has moved on, but she would not want you to cry, but instead celebrate the life and love that she instilled in everyone she came in contact with. Can I get an Amen? People?"

"We are all here, whether closely related or just friends, we will miss Grandma Nah-Nah. I would like to personally thank the family for choosing me to give this Eulogy about Mrs. Neliah Marie Baptiste, also known as Grandma Nah-Nah. I thank you, and God bless you all."

After Pastor Haywire was finished, there was nobody that wasn't crying in the church. He walked off the pew to Nah-Nah casket and kissed my grandma on the cheek. The church choir stood by waiting for their cue, and when he gave it, they sang some of Grandma's favorite songs. I remember being younger, and Grandma would hum those church songs all day.

Uncle Phil took the stage and told his testimony. He was like a pastor in training the way he spoke. A few other people spoke, and while the choir finished out, Auntie Ket-Ket was in the front row tripping as usual. When they closed the casket, she fell to the ground screaming at the top of her lungs. She called out to my mother a couple of times, like my mother would magically walk through the door. I looked at Avia, who sat next to me with tears in her eyes, hoping that Auntie would stop.

I never thought twice about going to the hospital to see my mother's body. Auntie Ket-Ket went to see my mother that morning for herself, making us late for the funeral. Uncle Phil tried to tell Aunt Ket-Ket that my mother was gone, but she didn't care. She insisted on seeing for herself. It was crazy, believe me. Everybody was going back to the house after the funeral. There, Uncle Phil was going to let everybody else know they had to get ready for another funeral.

• • •

The coleus flowers sat between my fingers. I twirled them through each finger, careful not to break them off their stems as I went down the small shrubs in front of my house. My mother planted them with patience. It took her a while, but she had the garden just the way she liked it.

"What are you doing?" Kadisha asked, coming outside after me.

Caught up in all the stuff that was going on, I didn't even notice how slowly my little sister was becoming a young lady. It seemed time flashed before me, and she was all of a sudden older. This was her first year at Norland Middle, and she was doing well in school. She was always trying to do her best. She came home one time with a C and cried her eyes out because she thought she was going to get in trouble. When she confided in me, I let her know it was alright. It was funny to me. I hadn't brought a report card home from school in I don't know how long. For what? I hadn't been to school in months, so it wasn't a secret what my grades looked like.

"Tryna get away from all that noise in the house. I should be asking you what you doing out here, jit. I meant little kid.

"I ain't no jit, boy, you better quit calling me that," she said, heading towards me.

I stopped at the crotons and fanned through them like my mother did. She used to dig through that stuff like an expert, pruning meticulously through her garden. She had the whole house looking like an island with all those colorful flowers and plants everywhere.

"Leave them alone, you know mama doesn't like us

playing around her stuff," Disha playfully slapped my hand away from the flowers.

I looked at her long and hard. She looked back like she was serious, then smiled. Her eyes reminded me of my Grandma's, and her round face was like my mother's. It sent chills up my arms and through my neck. I sat on a stump next to the flowers, looking out into the streets. She sat next to me; both our bodies barely able to fit in on the small space. Avia walked out the door to where we were sitting.

"There you'll go, I was just looking for you guys. Mahkahi, LZ, called and said he was coming. He gotta make a stop in the V for something and said that you'll know what he is talking about."

"Alright, thank you, but um, give me a minute, I need to talk to my sister," I said, looking up at her.

I knew exactly what LZ was talking about, and I couldn't wait to get back on Cloud 9.

"Oh, OK, I have to help Aunt Marie with the food anyway, you'll want something?" she asked.

"Nah, I'm good, you want something, Disha?" I said, bumping her with my elbow.

She looked like she was staring into space.

"No, not until you eat," Kadisha said, looking at me, then at Avia.

Avia made her way back into the house. I hadn't told Kadisha what was going on with our mother, so I was going to break it down to her.

"Hey, Disha, I need to talk to you about something. You know the last couple of days have been kinda crazy, and we have been going through all this stuff. I don't get a chance to talk to you about mama...."

"I know, Kahi," she acknowledged.

"You know what?" I asked, looking at the side of her face. She was looking toward the ground. She had a piece of the coleus flower folded in half in her hand.

"I know mama died," she said. "I heard them talking this morning when Auntie Marie and Uncle Phil came to the house." Her face showed her pain. "I'm sad, but I have to be strong. I cried a lot already, but I'll be alright," she continued to say.

I couldn't believe what I was hearing; the way she was talking made me want to breakdown.

"She told me one day if something was to ever happen to her, that you are all I got. She said you will protect me and do whatever you have to do to make sure I eat. She said, "You will protect me no matter what, and to respect you."

She never looked up. She sounded like she had taken our mother's word right out of her mouth. My mother had told me the same exact thing.

"I'll do like mama said, don't worry about that," I replied, putting my hand on her head, pulling her closer to me.

"Come on, man, you messing up my hair, jit," she said, laughing, slapping my hand away.

We talked a little about school. She asked me a few questions about where we would live and where Francia was going to live. I didn't know how to answer them, so I told her honestly that I didn't know. We heard a commotion coming from the house.

"He just told us she passed! I can't believe this shit, girl. No. She just helped me get better from pneumonia. My God, this ain't right, it isn't fair." She paced the front yard and walked down the street, still talking on the phone. She was so caught up in her conversation, she didn't see us sitting on the stump.

Kadisha was in her own world. I couldn't help but think about how I was going to make this better. I would surely try, but like they say, 'You got to go out and make shit happen.'

CHAPTER TWENTY-FIVE

September 11, 2001

I checked every room after waking up. I thought to myself that everybody must have left. It was a weekday, so I didn't really expect to catch anybody there anyway. I fixed a big bowl of cereal and sat in the living room on the couch, thinking about what I wanted to do for that day. Lately, I have been on some shit. Nobody was ready to give me anything, so I had to go out and take it. Monte and Ace went out with me on occasions, but when I learned the game, I went myself.

I ran into Rah G on my way to pull a caper in Carol City, one late night. I rode past this little corner store, and there he was, jumping out of a blue car with dark tinted windows. He had grown shoulder-length locks that were thick and bushy, covering his head. I recognized him from the way he was walking. He was like a young nigga with an old school vibe.

"Damn my nigga, what's happening, fool?' I yelled, pulling up to the store. He had this mug on his face and reached for his waist, backing away from the car. He squinted, trying to see who it was calling him.

"Oh shit! My nigga Megaman, what's good, fool?" he said when he recognized me.

"I'm straight, I see you on point, my nigga," I said, waving my gun so he could see.

I still had on some gloves I used to drive the stolen car I was in, and a ski mask was rolled up on top of my head like a Baggy Beanie. "What the fuck are you doing around here, kid, you are a long way from the hood," I told them. I hadn't seen him in a while, but to see him way in this area made me question what he was up to.

"I will stay around here. I am staying in the A.P.T.," he said, pointing to the apartment buildings down the street.

"My old girl moved around here not too long ago. I'm Lil Haiti bred though, nigga you know that. That's your whip, nigga?" Rah asked, checking out the car. It was a late model Maxima with a spoiler kit with nice tires. I stole it close to the V but planned to strip the parts and sell it to a chop shop in the hood when I was done with it.

"Nah, kid, this was stolen. I'm tryna get my bread up," I said honestly.

"Damn, bro, is that it? Some shit never surprises me, bro. You need to get down with me on this hustling shit. Let me write my beeper number down really quick," he said, getting ready to walk in the store.

"Yo Rah, jump in the whip, I got shit to write with," I said, remembering I saw a pencil somewhere around the car.

"My girl is in the car over there," he said, pointing at the late model Chevy in the parking space in front of me. "Let me get some rolling papers, and I'll be out in a minute. Do you need something?" Rah asked, still rushing to get in the store.

"Nah tighten up though, I gotta make some moves."

"Alright," he said, taking off.

Rah wasn't bullshitting. I thought eventually he was gonna leave the street life alone. He was headfirst in the game. He talked about taking over Carol City with the dope game. He ran some numbers by me. I didn't understand but said he would explain what he was trying to do later.

I thought about asking him if he had seen Kirby or Fatboy Tre, but I kept it to myself. We exchanged beeper numbers after I told him about the shit I was on.

"That shit is gonna get you killed," was all he said.

"I got to get it how I live, fool, my plate ain't looking right, a nigga is starving out here," I told him. He understood where I was coming from. Now that I think about it, I did it all; snatch purses, broke into homes, sold dope, and occasionally robbed people at ATMs. I did anything to put a dollar in my pocket. Shit was rough.

"Shit bro. Imma hit you up for real, just be looking for my number fool." That was all Rah said before we parted ways.

• • •

After we buried my mother, the whole family structure seemed like it was built on sand. The wind came along and blew us apart. Simon took Francia to stay with him, which the rest of the family thought was a crazy idea, and it caused arguments. By taking her away, it was going to break us up. Then they came up with the craziest idea. Aunt Marie wanted me to come to stay with her, while Aunt Ket-Ket wanted Kadisha to go with her.

First of all, I wasn't about to go to Aunt Marie's house. I loved them and all that, but they were too into that church thing. Second, Disha was my responsibility. I owed that to my mother to make sure Disha was good, so there was no way they were going to split us up. Not if I could help it. Lastly, I knew nobody wanted to keep all three of us anyway. Kadisha and I ended up with Auntie Ket-Ket. The family ended up slitting everything amongst each other, from my mother's pantyhose to her car. Her kids got nothing.

I decided to turn on the TV, flipped through a couple of channels when the breaking news hit the screen. I wasn't worried about no breaking news. The camera was focused on two tall buildings, and one of them was on fire. I changed the channel, and every station was on the same shit. Even BET! All this excitement.

I had to wait for Rah to page me. We had a long conversation. He said he was going to get at me that day. I just didn't know what time. When we did eventually talk, we picked up right where we left off. He had a spot in Carol City, and he wanted to put me on to get some of this dope money.

At first, I wasn't open to it, but I thought about all the money I had saved and how I ended up blowing it on having to provide for myself. I was tired of this robbing shit. Everybody I fucked with was in jail. LZ was in a Level 6 Program called Baypoint, and he wasn't coming home for another year. Monte got Direct File along with Big D, and Ace. They were in the country jail, facing serious charges of robbery. The judge wanted to sentence them as adults, sending them to prison for a long time, but their lawyer fought against it.

Lil V was in Haiti with his dad. He was wilding out, and his dad said he needed a break from the states. Even though he was born here, he took him there to straighten him out. Lil V told me before he found out he had to go to Haiti, he thought his dad had that work. He saw some stuff he wasn't supposed to see, and wanted to talk to me about it, but never got the chance.

Bored, I walked out the door, rolled a joint, and walked down the block. Auntie Ket-Ket stayed in North Miami. The streets were usually quiet around here. But today, it was too quiet, which felt strange.

After I smoked my joint, I went back to the house, got all the snacks I needed in case I got the munchies, and prayed that stupid shit was off the TV. To my surprise, it wasn't. I decided to turn the volume up to hear what the news anchor was so excited about. It was September eleventh, and The World Trade Center in New York had been hit by two planes. When I was watching the TV the first time, there was only one building on fire, but now both were on fire. They said terrorists attacked the United States and ran planes into the buildings. No wonder the streets were empty. People were in their houses, watching the events unfold.

My beeper went off. It was Rah hitting me with the code to get ready. I was happy. I had a plan, and it included leaving Auntie's house as soon as possible, for good! There was too much going on at my aunt's house. Kadisha and I had to share a room again, plus my aunt had family problems, and we just fell in the middle of it. They say you don't know somebody until you've lived with them. She and her husband were at war and slept in separate beds. Aunt Ket-Ket slept in the room that was supposed to be mine. Her husband slept in the master bedroom. Their kids shared a room next to his. The house was cluttered with people. Kadisha and I were too old to share a room together. I wasn't trying to live like that no more. I felt like I was going back in time. I made it my business to try to get up out of there.

• • •

Rah G had been trying this for a while now, from what he told me. He had this thing down to a science. He talked about renting a house, having dope friends come to the window like they did in the hood. He said around here, nobody was doing that. People did hand-to-hand transactions in the middle of the streets. That's why they were getting caught and going to jail all the time.

We rode around the A.P.T. where he stayed, and he showed me some of the spots the guys in the neighborhood had, and how they ran them.

"Look at that dumb-ass nigga right there, fool," he said.

We parked the car where nobody would notice. He said nobody paid attention to what was going on; they were just thirsty. A guy came out of the building to a waiting car, while one man on a bike pulled up at the same time. Right there, he did two sales, in the same parking lot out in the open.

"See, we can't be stupid like that nigga there. We needed a crib, but we got to get the bread to do it. How much money you got saved?" he asked me.

"I ain't got nothing, fool. I had to use the money I had to feed Disha and me, and at the same time, I got a shoe fetish, fool," I admitted.

"We have to plot on something big, then get us an apartment that's for rent. They go for about five hundred rounds here."

"Five Hundred. Fool, that's a grip," I exclaimed. "I could come up with half, though."

"I know you can. Five hundred for the crib, and it's going to be two grand for some real work. We already know how to get the fiends to the house, the same way we used to get them to come to the bleachers," he said, smiling.

"Damn, the bleachers. I remember that shit, fool," I replied, thinking about the past.

"The hood is crazy, bro. Niggas dying left and right," he explained. "I ain't seen none of them nigga we grew up with," he said, passing me his joint.

He let the smoke fill his lungs as he pulled out of the parking spot.

"My old girl said fuck it' and moved from around EL Portal and didn't let me visit my Grandma no more. She fell on hard times and had to get an apartment here in these buildings. I have been tryna do the same," he said, passing the joint back to me, resting his head on the headrest.

"That house you came and got me from, that's my aunt's house. My old girl passed away, fool," I announced, turning my head to face him.

He almost choked on the smoke as he inhaled it.

"Say what? When did this shit happen, kid?" He said, looking from me to the road ahead.

"She just got sick all of a sudden and died from pneumonia. I got to get my sister and me out of this situation, fool. I mean whatever it is gonna take, I'm up for it. I'm tired of staying in North Miami at my aunt's place," I complained.

"I heard that. We are gonna make this move. When we open up shop, we are gonna buss all the work down to the smallest rocks. Nickel bags. We are gonna be the youngest niggas selling five-dollar rocks way up this way. Watch," he bragged.

He seemed to fall in deep thought for a minute. My high was settling in, and I wasn't much for words now that I was feeling it. "I gotta take this whip back to my people, where are you headed?" he asked.

"Shit, I guess back to the house," I replied, hating the thought of it.

We rode the rest of the way in silence. I thought about telling him about my grandma passing too, but some things are better off kept to yourself. I wasn't in the business of making people feel sorry for me. All I needed was the right motivation, and I was back on. I felt like I needed to unleash that hustler's ambition. I knew I had it in me, but for some reason, I couldn't bring it out. I didn't have time for shit else; school, auntie, nothing. The only thing I had time for was counting them Franklins. I ain't care if it took me a lifetime to finish, all the money in my world needed to be in a pile, and up under me.

While I was out trying to get my money, I ran into a wall. My relationship with Auntie Ket-Ket was complicated. I didn't want to go to school. School wasn't an option for me. I had bigger fish to fry. My mind was on trying to get this money the fast way, and by any means necessary. Besides, why show up at school when I had nothing to show for? It ain't like I had the right clothes and shoes. I felt like if it wasn't making me any money now, then it was a waste of time. She had the nerve to go off on me about a game and TV that I bought.

"Mahkahi, you're going to have to get out and do something with yourself, get a job, or something. I can't have you sitting up in my house all day doing nothing. We work around here, and your sister goes to school. All you want to do is run the streets, eat, sleep, and shit," Auntie Ket-Ket said, standing over me.

I did have something to do. I was sick and tired of the nagging. It took a lot out of me not to give her a piece of my mind right then. I tried to be a little passive.

"Auntie, can you move please, you blocking my view. I can't see the TV," I asked her politely.

She snapped.

"No. You are going to listen to what I have to say. You are in my house. If you don't like it… hold the fuck up…I'm blocking your view?" she asked, laughing. "The last time I checked Mahkahi, I'm grown. And not only that, I pay all the bills around here," she said, fanning her hand in circles. "As a matter of fact, turn the television off, now!"

I took a long look at her questioningly. This lady was crazy, I thought. I had to think about what she was saying. She was going out of her way to get on my nerves.

"Why are you always jumping down on my throat, Auntie?" I asked, not able to hold back anymore. I had to give this woman a piece of my mind. I threw the controller on the side of the bed where I was sitting. "Today this, tomorrow you find something else to talk about. Damn! I heard you, but I don't even bother nobody," I said, blowing air out of my nose, frustrated.

"I don't even bother nobody," she said, mocking me. "You. Don't. Do. Nothing at all. Come on, get up, and cut that shit off. You're going to do the yard. I have something for you to do. Go ahead and cut them off, I ain't gonna tell you again," she reiterated.

"Hold up, man, I ain't no slave to nobody," I protested, standing up. "You can't make me do no yard on your time. My mama would've never made me do no shit like that." I slipped and cursed at her unconsciously.

Her face was contorted with anger. Her light skin turned beet red.

"I'm not your fucking mama. Your mama is dead," she yelled. Spit flew out of her mouth as she spoke. I had struck a nerve. "Listen to me, Mahkahi," she said, pointing in my face. "You better not curse at me like that again. You get your shoes on and get your ass outside now and cut my grass or get your shit and get the fuck out."

"No, I ain't cutting no grass!"

"Then, get out!" she repeated." I gave you a chance, you

didn't take it. Get out. I can't teach you how to be a man. You have to learn that on your own. I'm not in any shape to be going through this with you. No, not me," she said, closing her eyes, shaking her head.

"Alright then," I said, putting on my shoes. My pride wouldn't let me bow down like that. My auntie ain't mean no harm. She was trying to teach me a lesson, but just like her, I wasn't going for it. I was still healing in a way, and I was feeling the press game. She wanted me to feel her anger, and if it meant getting my shit, and getting out, then I was going to do just that.

"Hurry the fuck up, and get all your shit too," she said, snatching the plugs out of her wall.

Her anger reminded me of my mother that day when she came home early, and I had all those people in her house. She walked over to the closet and threw my clothes and shoes on the floor.

She is dead serious...but she is going too far with it.

"Don't throw my shit on the floor. What are you doing? You ain't buy none of that stuff. You are tripping man," I snapped.

"What are you going to do, huh? What are you going to do, hit me?" she said, getting inches away from my face. "Get out," she said.

I didn't have the heart to put my hands on a woman, let alone a woman in my own family. The anger I felt wasn't safe for either of us, so I turned on my heel and left. As I walked the dark streets, I thought about calling Rah G, but once again, my pride got in the way. I had a few dollars in my pocket, and there was one place I knew for sure I was always welcomed.

• • •

Walking up 172nd street, I thought of a good excuse to visit LZ's mother and father. I was stressed out, no place to sleep, I needed to rest my nerves, at least for the night. My mind was so full of thoughts, I couldn't think of anything solid to say. I thought to myself what I would say. All I could think about was my situation and how I had to suffer the consequences of the cards I was dealt with. I wondered if Auntie and I would ever get along again. After what just happened, I doubted it. My mom and Aunt Ket-Ket had a falling out before, and it took them over two years to reconcile.

"Hey, Mrs. Robiou, how are you doing?" I asked. She seemed happy to see me but was curious about the late-night visit.

"What are you doing out so late?" she asked, looking out onto the street. I was lost for words for a second.

"Got locked out and was wondering if I could spend the night? I don't know when anybody was coming home, and I don't know where I could reach them to call. So, I caught the bus here.

"You kids," she sighed. "I'm glad you came over here and not out there getting in no trouble. This house has been emptied since Emmanuel and Alex went to jail," she said, referring to LZ and Ace by their first names. Come inside. My husband is in there, sleeping."

Good lord, he would want to ask me so many questions. Good thing, he sleeps hard. I'll explain it to him in the morning.

Kevlon is in his room watching a movie. Go ahead and make yourself comfortable," she finally said.

"Thank you," I said, stepping inside.

I walked into Trigga's room. He was so caught up in the movie, he barely heard me walk in.

"What's good, hood?" I asked. The room was dark except for the light on the TV. Had it not been on, I doubt I would have been able to see anything.

"Ain't nothing, just watching Scarface and shit. How did you get in the house?" he asked nonchalantly, never taking his eyes off the TV.

"I walked in the back door. You should keep that shit locked," I said playfully, sitting next to him. That got his attention, and he turned around to see if I was serious.

"Who let you in nigga, because I locked it myself?" he said, sitting up, turning on the lamplight beside him. "My old girl must've let you in. That lady ain't never sleep."

"Yeah, she let me in. I walked all the way over here, fool. My Auntie and I went through it again, that shit got ugly, fool."

"Damn, you walked all the way from over there in North Miami. What happened, what is she tripping about now?"

"For real, bro, it ain't even worth talking about. She went off on me, I went off back, and she told me to get out," I said. I felt some type of way for something so petty to be the reason I got kicked out of my aunt's house.

"Fuck all that, though. What's up with Ace and Dem, the bro? What are they gonna do with their niggas?"

"I don't know, fool. Nobody told us nothing. The last time I saw him was at this court hearing. They said something about five years ago, but they ain't have a gun or no DNA. They got a ski mask that was at the scene, but Ace said he had dumped him, and LZ came home soon after the program. Ace might beat that shit though, bro," he said, shrugging his shoulders. His attention was back on the TV.

For the next couple of days, Trigga and Six hid the fact that I slept at the house. I didn't want to wear out my welcome. As the days went by, it got easier to come over. Their father and mother split up over the weeks. Trigga told me that his father got caught cheating on his mother. I guess my bad luck was rubbing off on all the people around me. I needed to go see the voodoo lady. She had a special bath that would cleanse your body with water that ward off evil spirits. That's exactly what I needed.

Every day I wake up ready to hit the streets. I had to leave the house when everybody was gone. Mrs. Robiou thought I was going to school, and I had to play it like that. After seeing me there all the time, she became comfortable with me being at the house. She wasn't tripping on me being there. She only asked that I call home every now and then, which I didn't do, but told her I did. It was hard-hitting the streets daily like that. I had nothing to do. I was alone, going broke, without a plan in the world. I couldn't keep playing these stray puppy games. Police in NMB roamed the streets faithfully.

I got desperate and broke into a few houses, coming up on shit I could carry by hand. After a while, I stumbled on a small gun. Breaking into houses got too risky. I was either going to get money or starve. I had to become a wolf in sheep clothing. I planned to use my baby face as a tool to go unnoticed, so I could walk upon the perfect pick.

CHAPTER TWENTY-SIX

I parked the stolen car around the corner from the mall, out of sight where it would blend in with all the other cars in the building parking lot. Before that, I went through LZ's dresser drawers. I found some already shaved keys. Soon as I saw them, the light bulb in my brain went on. I ended up scoping the mall parking lot for the perfect victim. All I wanted to do was find a woman, not too old or too young, who looked like they were holding some cash. I had to be picky about it.

No one too old because I had a bad experience one time with this old lady. I had to pry her hands off the purse because she was having a heart attack or something. I didn't want anyone young, because they liked to fight back, and barely had enough money for lunch. Besides, my hundred and fifteen-pound frame wasn't ready for a tussle.

I went through the mall's front entrance, looked around on the inside, and didn't see anything that caught my eye immediately. I kept scoping the mall until I saw the perfect person right across 163rd street. I had a problem, though; it was almost time for school to let out, and the traffic was heavy. My main goal was the mall parking lot, but some rules were meant to be broken. As hungry as I was, I was ready to climb a building to get to King Kong if he had what I wanted.

I watched a white woman in her mid-forties, kind of on the heavy side, get out of a caravan by herself. She walked into the plaza's check-cashing place.

"Jackpot!" I mouthed, hungrily to myself.

I hurried across the busy street and pretended to search for something on the ground. I almost got hit by two cars. I had on some Air Max 95's, black pants, and a nice Polo shirt to match my outfit, courtesy of LZ's closet. I had to dress like I belonged, rather than screaming 'I want to rob you.' I looked around nervously for the police and anybody who looked like they had the potential to be a hero. Heroes were worse than the police. They acted like they had fantasies about being a superhero, and when that time came, they did all they could to get noticed.

The coast was clear. Now I had to count on my speed to get me through this.

I got to the Caravan out of breath. I felt like I was running a marathon trying to beat this woman to her car. I crouched down acting like I was tying my shoes and must have timed it perfectly, because the car doors made the unlock noise. My heart raced as I got up to make my move. I was on the passenger door in a flash, she never saw me.

I saw the back of her head as she looked the other direction towards the mall. My mother had that habit, well most women did, never looking when they put their purse down in the seat. It was either the back seat or the passenger seat. Luck was on my side because she chose the passenger seat that day.

I grabbed the purse as if she was handing it to me. My adrenaline was at its peak. It was heavy too, one of those heavy-duty purses like she was a businesswoman or something. I put the small handles through my arm at lightning speed. I tucked the purse out of view and took off.

"Hey! Nooooo!" She screamed.

I was across the busy street in two skips and a hop. I went through the parking lot and walked towards the buildings getting closer to the car. I didn't look back for fear of looking suspicious. A black kid on a school day, running with a large purse in the middle of a parking lot, should have looked out of place. But I was a squirrel to everybody that walked by. Nobody looked my way. Not the lady that walked past me on her cell phone talking about child support, or the man with the package who ran past me leaving his van with the keys in the ignition. I thought about getting in his van, adding a little excitement to my day, but I kept walking with that schoolboy look. I kept my head low like I was confused as to where mama parked the car. Maybe my luck wasn't so buzzard, after all.

Just when I started the car, something zapped me on the side. I felt like I was going to shit on myself, it scared me so badly. I had a hard time putting the key in the ignition I was shaking so badly. It was the cell phone I just got going off. I had forgotten I had it with me.

At the same time, a ringing noise came from the purse. I ignored it, driving toward 15th avenue past Jiffy's. A bunch of police cars raced passed me going the other way. I kept my eyes straight on the road. If only they knew. When all ten of the police cars passed, I was able to exhale.

I took the pager off my waist and saw that Rah G had paged me, and he hit his code. He wanted to see me at 9:11. The phone kept ringing in the passenger seat, making me nervous. My phone keeps going off. First, I needed a safe place to park the car and had to find out if the purse was worth putting North Miami Beach on fire for the night. At the rate, I was going the streets were for sure going to be hot.

This lady had all kinds of shit in her purse. I went for the white envelopes and just as I suspected lottery! I counted three bundles of fifteen hundred dollars each in just one of the envelopes. Two bundles of five hundred in another, and seven hundred in a wallet. My eyes lit up like a Christmas tree looking at all this green. The phone kept going off in the purse. It was so full of shit; it was a mission to find it. I was too busy looking through shit to be bothered by a ringing phone.

I found a list with checks attached to it, another list with addresses, all of them in the same area we were just in. Some were apartments, and some were businesses. This bitch was probably a landlord collecting rent. When I saw the other envelope full of more checks, it sealed the deal. All of them were made out, adding up to thousands of dollars. I ain't care about no checks though, I wasn't trying to get caught up like that.

Then I remembered I had to call Rah G. I put all the cash together and counted the big bundles first, separating the one-hundred-dollar bills from the twenty-dollar bills, down to the smallest bills.

I was rich and already thinking about investing. I was glad I didn't have to invest in a ski mask.

• • •

"Rah, what's the 411, kid?" I said, speaking into the woman's phone. I planned on telling Rah G what happened, but not just yet.

"I'm in my building, fool, these niggas around here act like they want the pressure. I need you around here A.S.A.P. We gotta talk, fool," Rah said angrily. That put a dent into what I was thinking. Now, he sounded like he had problems that I didn't want to deal with.

"I'm on my way, I'm on the 15th kid, and I'll be there in a minute, just chill. Need me to bring that thing, so we could straighten them niggas around there?" I asked.

"Yeah, yeah, bring that. Is this your new number, fool?" he questioned.

"Nah, I'm using this bitch phone. We'll talk when I get there, though." I was about to hang up when I heard the line clicking on the other end. I looked at the phone screen, and someone was calling. I picked up against my better judgment.

"Hello! Please, sir, just bring the money back. My husband will kill me if I don't recover that money." The woman at the other end of the phone spoke very quickly.

The sound of her voice was crushing, she was desperate and on edge. I couldn't give the tiniest fuck, though. I didn't feel any remorse for what I was doing. If anything, I felt entitled to that money. Shit, I wasn't the one slipping.

"Are you alone?" I asked in a deep voice, trying my damnedest not to laugh.

"Hello," she said again. I could tell she put a hand over the receiver.

It sounded muffled on her end like someone was saying something to her, but I couldn't make out what they were saying. Then I heard the phone fumble and static from the air around her.

"Yeah. Yeah... I'm alone, sir, just please bring my things back, and I won't call the police. Listen... please, just listen before you say anything, sir," she said, pausing for a minute before she spoke again. "I'll give you some of the money, but I need those checks and most of my paperwork. Sir, just do the right thing, will you? I'm begging you to do the right thing."

I almost would have felt sorry for her, if my heart hadn't already turned black. The fire began to settle, but the path it left behind was already damaged.

"I probably need this money more than you and your husband need it. Since you lied to me."

"I didn't lie," she screamed. "Lie about what? I did not lie," she kept saying.

"Listen, when I speak, shut the hell up bitch," I said, between clenched teeth. I had to force myself to be mad. I wanted to laugh so badly. I was pretty good at this acting shit, I thought. "You lied, bitch, because you said you were alone. I saw the police go your way. Do you want to know something else?" I asked.

"Yes, what is it? But I swear, sir," she said, crying. She knew I caught her in a lie. She dropped to a whisper. "I'll tell them to go away. I promise the police made me do it this way. They told me what to say. But I'm sorry, just please, we can arrange for you to bring it to me, no police. Just me."

"Should've just told the truth, liar! Listen, Mrs. um…" I took a moment to grab the ID out of the purse sitting next to me. "Mrs. Blackmon, I know your name, address, and all the other information you left in this big-ass purse."

"Oh pleeease," she cried.

"Shut up and listen. Call me back, and you'll see me again!" I said, seriously. I wanted to sound like a threat. I hung up and put the phone and ID on the passenger seat. I put the cash on my lap and headed straight to Rah's apartment building.

Before I got on 826 to head West, I went by 172nd to grab the gun that I left. I prayed to God; I didn't have to use it. I had enough action for the day. The helicopters were in the air circulating like hungry vultures looking for a meal. I wasn't him. I moved as calmly as I could. Lucky for me, when I got to the house, no one was home.

When Rah saw me, he immediately stood up. I put

the bag I had in my hand on the floor. We high-fived each other like we always did, and he sat back down and started explaining the whole situation.

"This pussy-ass nigga named Russ from these apartments trying to check me about getting paper around here," he said quickly.

At the same time, he was eyeballing the bag that was on the floor, but he stuck to his script.

"Haven't you been getting money around here? What did he say that got you so amped up?" I asked, staring at him strangely. He was really in his feelings.

"See that hallway over there? Dreds got weed and shit over there," he said, pointing to his right. "The other hallway, Knot and Vamp and Dem got that," he said, pointing straight ahead. He kept mentioning these names like I knew who these people were.

"Who are the dreds, Vamp, Knot, and who is Russ supposed to be? The H.N.I.C?" I asked.

"All of them fuck-niggaz fuck with each other, bro. Russ got all the sack. Knot and Vamp work for Russ. Dreds got their own shit, but I ain't got no army. A bunch of niggaz around here already got their shit. I ain't from around here. I know that. I ain't tryna step on any of these niggaz toes. Feel me? I moved my shit from my apartment down that hallway. Russ got in my way. I ain't got that kinda time. Feel me? We got to see that boy! Get on some shoot um, bang-bang shit," he said.

"Man, you tripping. How are we gonna do that? We are a two-man team, fool. I only got this little shit, and this ain't enough," I said, patting the gun on my belt.

"Let me get that shit, I'm gonna kill the head, and the body is dead. Russ, the nigga who really feeds all them niggaz, with him out of the picture, niggaz know who did it.

Ain't nobody trying to fuck with some young killing-ass niggaz," he said, hitting his chest with his fist. "These niggaz got me twisted. Let me get that," he yelled.

Rah was really feeling himself.

"Listen, bro," I said, holding out my hand. "There's more than one way to skin a cat. Killing one nigga ain't gonna do nothing but start a war we ain't got no way of winning," I said seriously.

He shook his head, agreeing with me. His whole demeanor changed. "We're gonna eat, but we gotta play these niggaz from the back door. Let's get into this house. Imma tell you about it here," I said, picking up the bag heading towards his apartment.

The small apartment was clean. It smelled of fresh apples and cinnamon. The air outside smelled drug infested. It reminded me of Lil Haiti streets where island food and the smell of cooked crack mixed in the air. I thought about getting something like the apartment Rah, and his mom had for Kadisha and me when my money got straight. I hoped I would be able to come up with the money to take care of both of us.

I set the bag I had in my hand on the table and watched Rah, who was sitting on the couch across me, stare at me with a puzzled look. I saw him glancing at the dirty bag when we were outside talking. The conversation led up to this, and I know he was dying to know what was in this bag.

"Why the fuck is that bag so dirty, Megaman? Get that shit off my mom's table," he screamed. I picked up the bag off the table and turned it upside down, emptying its contents.

"How much money is that?" he asked in awe. Quickly he grabbed the hundred-dollar bundle. I packed them neatly

JEAN PETERSON | 219

after counting them. I put them in five-hundred-dollar bundles and put a thousand in my pocket for emergencies.

"That's fifty-two hundred right there. I made that shit
from one lick. I got my part of the money. Where's yours?"
I questioned.

"What lick, fool? He asked, thumbing through the
crispy bills, ignoring my question.

"Nigga, you worried about the wrong thing. I got it
right there in the flesh, nigga. That's all you need to know.
Where is your money?" I reiterated. He got up off the
couch, went to his room, and came back with a shoebox.

What's up with these niggaz and this shoebox stuff?

He pulled out neatly stacked bundles, each in sequences
of fives, tens, and one-dollar bills.

It was right then and there that I ran the plan down to
him. There was a saying that came to me while I spoke to
Rah about our plans. I remember Scoot telling me, 'You had
to build relationships before you made enemies.' I hadn't
given Scoot much thought until I had to run this plan of
ours down. We couldn't go to war and didn't have our
money right. Truthfully, I wasn't trying to go to war. I was
trying to get me some paper.

Life was taking me through a maze, but I had to find
my way to the cheese. I told Rah we weren't trying to take
over the apartments. We were just there to get a piece of
cake. We were going to let Russ run his business, and we
were valuable clientele. That way, we keep the peace. I figured since we would cop work from him, he wasn't going
to be tripping if we pushed the same shit here.

"What if he tries to takes the money and shit?" he asked.

"Then you kill the head and get the fuck from around
here. I'll be damned if a nigga takes anything from me," I
retorted, patting the gun.

I told Rah to come up with the numbers for the next couple of days. We needed to come up with a good spot out of everybody way so we could sell our drugs. We would go big, and at the end of the day, everything else would fall in place. The way I looked at it, I've burnt before, and a loss to me was a minor setback for a major comeback. One thing was for sure, I wasn't going out without a fight. I told Rah to holla at the dreads and set up a meeting with Russ's people.

Two days later…

"First thing first, we are going fifty-fifty on everything Megaman. A split straight down the middle," Rah said, slashing his hand like a sword. "I already holla at the dreads like you told me to. They ain't tripping, if we ain't short stopping on their shit with the weed. They say, 'Man don't worry about a thing,' he said in his fake Jamaican accent. "I also talked to one of Russ' people and let the nigga know I'm trying to talk to them. He said he was gonna relay the message."

"What else did you say?" I asked him.

Rah G had the tendency to run off at the mouth a little too much. Something I noticed when we were on the phone the other day. He sat there and told whoever he was talking to how he would call her back because he was counting stacks. He made the money whistle on the receiver so she could hear it. I had a long talk with him after that day. I wasn't trying to get robbed over stupidity.

"I ain't tell the nigga shit, only that we had to talk to them. Why?" he asked.

"Nothing. I have meant to tell you, bro, we need to get a bucket. I'm tired of catching the fucking bus," I said.

"A bucket? Ain't none of us got no license, fool," he said truthfully. None of us had a license, but I had to get around. I ain't have time to worry about a license. "Fuck all that, we could worry about a license later. We are gonna go over there. let me talk to this nigga, Russ. And when we touch some extra change, we got a bucket both of us could use."

"Alright. I came up with the numbers. Let me run it down to you really quick," he said, using his fingers as examples. This is fifty-five hundred; it is only gonna cost us seven hundred a zip. That small shit we had back in the days ain't near what we can make off each zip. We gonna make a stack if we cut them into nickel rocks. At seven hundred a zip, if we got fifty-five hundred, we could buy, let's say…" He stopped to think for a minute, looking up in the air, mumbling something to himself, tapping his left hands over his right palm" …six zips. Really like five because we are gonna get the sixth one for free."

"I'm saying, if we are only buying five zips, five ain't nothing but thirty-five hundred. How about the rest of the money?" I asked.

"Hold up, fool, let me finish. We need bags, scales, a safe, another apartment to sell this shit because my mama's house is out of the question. That is gonna cost us two-thousand. We hustle hard enough for a month, flip everything twice, and do it all over again till we figure out what to do with the cushion."

I sat halfway listening to him. All these extra costs weren't part of the plan. We needed the bucket too, and it proved once again that the more money, the more problems.

"And don't forget the twenty-five-dollar fee to cook it up, Megaman," he said finally.

I wondered if I should tell this nigga that Scoot taught

me how to cook dope. If we were going to save money, I had to figure out a way to tell him.

"Don't worry about the twenty-five, we could scratch it. Let me handle it."

"What do you mean, let you handle it? Do you know somebody who is gonna charge us less?"

"You are looking at him. Like I said, let me handle it, nigga. What do you think? Imma fuck it up?" I asked. I wasn't even sure if I wouldn't fuck it up. I hadn't thought about cooking dope, let alone selling it until I ran into this nigga.

"Whatever you say fool, I trust you, you ain't let me down yet," Rah G assured.

Now all I needed to do was trust myself. From then on, we never looked back. At first, shit was slow, but the quality of the dope made shit get better. I was able to make it come back like it was supposed to.

• • •

I went to North Miami Middle School in search of my sister, Kadisha. I hadn't seen her in a couple of months after the fight with my Aunt Ket-Ket. I caught her walking a few blocks from Ket-Ket's house. After giving her some pocket money, she told me life at Ket-Ket's was unbearable and that she wanted to stay with me. She was highly upset when I told her that I had a lot of shit going on and that as soon as I was on my feet, we would stay together. I left my sister with a kiss on her forehead with promises of a cell phone in the near future.

After I ran all my errands, I decided to ride through Lil Haiti to holla with a few people. Scoot was one I missed— the old fart. I wanted to give him a few dollars and my phone number. The money was coming in slowly. We were still able to get the bucket in no time. We got a new phone to spread the word. As I headed south on I-95, I thought back on how I got to this point.

• • •

"Ok, you said, bring two, to apartment 211, and four to the lady that is with Ma June," Rah G repeated after me.

I had a few things to do and asked him to handle orders for me since I was stepping out. Everything was going our way. We had our own work and ran our business like our lives depended on it.

"Imma go make these few stops before I come back. Do you need anything while I'm out?" I asked Rah while he was in the kitchen, bagging up some of the rocks.

We tagged our black baggies with yellow smiley faces since the corner store only sold baggies in four colors. Everybody that sold crack in the building was already using all the colors, so I came up with the stickers to set us apart.

"Nigga, I'm good, go ahead," he yelled from the kitchen.

During the weekdays, we set up shop at his mother's house because she was at work. Ma June was a smoker whose house we used on the weekends when his mama was home. Ma June wasn't a friend like most people I knew who smoked crack. She was a smoker that went to work, paid her rent on time but loved to get high. She also did a little hustling with food when the crack heads came down from their highs, for a small fee of course. She was an older woman who had an apartment all by herself and didn't mind renting a room out. Everybody in the apartments fucked with Ma June.

She took a liking to me one day when I helped her with groceries. She surprised me when she said, "I know what you are doing, and I'd love to help you out for a small fee."

Ma June became my go-to lady when the police came around or when I wanted to crash at her place with Avia. Ma June welcomed me with open arms. Avia was blind to my criminal activities. I lied to her and told her Ma June was my mother's best friend. We were getting money, and it was time to spread my wings. It all fell in order, and we were coming up, meeting the right people, and making all the right moves.

• • •

I rounded the corner of Zuby's Supermarket, where I thought Scoot would be, but there was no sign of him. I decided to ride through my old block on the 55th. I turned into my father's old parking space, taking in the memory of the old block. Everything was still the same. It seemed as if the old paint on the walls was still holding on. The streets were dry except for the two people walking my way from a distance. I sat there a minute waiting until they got closer. Fiends hustle day and night, sometimes for days and nights waiting for their opportunity to score bigger and bigger for their next hit. Boy, oh, boy! They have been in the streets for such a long time that they forget to shower. They don't sleep or eat.

When they got closer, I couldn't believe my eyes. Black Barbie saw me getting out of the car. She started to put on a show, dusting herself and swinging her short nappy hair. I watched her awkwardly sway back and forth, trying to look sexy.

I stepped away from the car before she got closer. I didn't want her dirty ass staining anything I owned with her filth. When we stood face to face, she kept her eyes focused on something else. That's when I knew she didn't know who I was.

"She ain't with me, I'm solo," she smiled, flashing a mouth full of missing teeth.

She went from ugly to disgustingly ugly. She lost her behind, she had sores on her arms, and her nails were dirty beyond repair. She was looking like a walking corpse waiting to get buried.

"You tryna party because I ain't got all day," she said, impatiently.

"Nah, I ain't tryna party, Black Barbie," I said, getting her attention. She looked at me through squinted eyes, coming closer. I had to move back because the smell coming from her was unbearable. I thought she was going to say she recognized me, but she didn't.

"What you holding because I ain't got no money, but if you want me to suck your dick for a hit, we can't stand out here," she said. She scratched her dry scalp and licked her lips. I was uncomfortable.

"Black Barbie. What's up with you, you don't remember me?" I said, looking at her. "This Scoot homie, Megaman. I moved away from here a long time ago."

She looked at me through squinted eyes. I let her get a little closer this time. I changed a little physically, but I pretty much looked the same.

"No!" she said, putting her dirty hands to her mouth. "Little man, that used to come to my house? Boy! You are sexy," she said, stepping back to take a good look at me. "You are now big and shit. Boy, hug your auntie."

I stepped back, giving her a look that read, 'don't touch me.'

I'm sorry, honey," she said, rubbing her head. She looked around, embarrassed.

I looked past her to see what Fatboy's mother was

doing. She was still on the ground, sitting Indian style, playing with something she found.

"Well, Scoot almost killed both of us. But he died first," she said, getting my attention.

I know this bitch ain't just offer me no head and say what I think she just said.

"Dead!" I reiterated. "You mean to tell me he is dead?"

"Yep. What? You haven't heard, G? Gave me and that bitch over there that bug. We're dead in a little. I need something to ease the pain, baby, Auntie is sick," she said cringing.

"How long?" I asked.

"How long has Scoot been dead?"

"Just a few weeks. His body couldn't hold AIDS. It ate him up," she said. I could tell she wasn't comfortable talking about it because she avoided eye contact, shifting from one leg to the other.

There was no more to be said. I came, got the answers I was looking for, and it was time to go. I reached in my pocket, peeled a few dollars from my bundle to compensate her for her time, and threw it at her. The bills blew around some. She ran for the bills as they floated down in the wind. I watched her in disgust as she managed to catch every single dollar.

When I got back in the car, I put my head on the steering wheel. *AIDS?* I was numb to the pain. I felt none. My days of mourning death were over. More than anything, I wished I could get to him before he died. I looked in the rearview mirror, and the two women were arguing. Black Barbie kept her hands behind her back. Tre's mother tried to reach behind, knowing Barbie had either money or dope in her hands. They tried their best to mask their pain with that glass dick. I drove off and headed back home. I took the on-ramp and headed north, back to where I came from.

CHAPTER TWENTY-SEVEN

"**A**in't this about a bitch," I said to myself. KP and Pouchon stood face to face with Russ, holding a deep conversation when I pulled into the apartments. Behind tinted windows, I couldn't be seen. The last time I saw KP was when he put us on that sour lick at Pico's. When Pouchon got out, nobody cared about what was going on with him. Everybody was trying to make their own move. Rarely did I see these two together, and from the looks of it, the conversation was private. One thing I figured out about this nigga KP was that he was dead serious about his money and was going to get it by any means.

I parked the car around the back to avoid being seen by either one of those guys. The only conversation I needed was with Russ. I needed to know when to drop off and when to pick up. I made my way through the apartments to Ma June's. Before I went to talk to Rah G, someone yelled my name.

"Megaman, what's up, fam?"

I looked around the empty hallway.

I didn't see anyone, so I kept walking. The voice yelled out again, and that's when I saw Uno quickly walking towards me from one of the apartment doors.

"What's up, fam? Why are you following me, nigga? He asked playfully.

When he smiled, four new gold crowns shined on his front teeth like yellow piss.

"Probably, nigga, you might be following me. Everywhere I go, you there, fool," I said.

First, KP, then Pouchon, and now I saw this nigga. I knew these niggas were up to something. I kept my game face on.

"I'm with KP and Dem. They are outside, talking to some nigga. I fuck with a bitch named Natalie. You know her, she stays here," he said, pointing towards a door I was familiar with.

I ignored the comment about KP.

"Nah, I don't think I do," I lied. Natalie was a freak that I had a few run-ins with, but I didn't want to expose my hand. "I just came to holla at one of my dawgs. Imma let you do you, though. Fuck with me, cuzzo," I said, cutting the conversation short.

"Alright, put my number on your phone. It ain't a coincidence we keep running into each other, fool. I see you looking sporty and shit," he said.

He stepped back, pointing at my new patent leather Jordans.

"Shit, you are the one shining, fool, grilled up and shit," I said. "Check this out, Uno. Get at me, my nigga. We have a lot to talk about."

Our eyes never broke contact. For some reason, I didn't like the idea of my cousin fucking with KP. I knew KP was capable of fucking over anybody. Soon, I would try and figure out what was going on between Russ and them.

• • •

I walked into Ma June's house, and the powerful smell of the Cush joint hit my nose immediately. I used the key she gave me to let myself in. Ma June wasn't home, and the house was full of people I've seen before but didn't care to acknowledge. I walked straight to the backroom that Rah and I rented. Scoot was heavy on my mind; I couldn't think of anything else. I really wasn't trying to deal with the fact that he was dead.

When I walked into my room, I threw the keys on the frameless mattress that sat on the floor. I thought about calling Rah and telling him to come to help me with what I was about to do but decided against it. I needed some time to think and didn't need any distractions.

I went to the small closet, reached up to the ceiling, pulling out the light bulb. I unscrewed the screws that held up the bulb. Behind the wires, I pulled out the little sack that held our dope, then put the bulb and mount back in its place. I sat in the sack on the closet floor, then went to set up the microwave and scale. I needed to fetch some ice out of the kitchen. I put everything in its place and pulled the dope out of the sock. I only had four and a half ounces left and needed to stretch it as far as it would let me. I put everything on the scale, and it weighed out evenly like the last time I saw it; a hundred and twenty-eight grams.

I pulled the cup I used to cook my dope out of the dresser drawer along with some cut for the dope. The cut was used to stretch the dope. I was going to see if Russ was just talking the talk. He promised me this new batch would be raw and uncut; said he gave it to me because I would know how to get all my money back and some. I don't know where he got that idea from, but as sure as hell is hot, I was going to make ends meet.

Scoot's name wasn't going to go out in vain. I was going to represent the old head. All the shit he taught me came down to this. I stopped for a minute, looking around the room, missing something. Then it hit me, baking soda and the music.

After I mixed the dope with the recommended amount of cut, my finished product spoke volumes. Russ didn't just talk the talk; his ass made shit happen. Everything came back like it was supposed to. I shook out the last cookie out of its jar. I picked up the solid circle of a rock, it shined crystals on its surface. I picked it up and scanned its purpose and thought to myself,

How could someone let this shit be the master of their thoughts?

I knew we needed to go bigger. In the streets, as I saw it, there was a demand, then supply. I had to talk to Rah G about our next move. In reality, I wanted to expand. Truthfully, I wasn't trying to stay cooped up in the apartments all day. My young mind was on the bigger picture.

My phone began to ring, interrupting my thoughts. Avia's number flashed on the screen. I closed my eyes thinking of the last time we were together, alone. It's almost like it was a one-way relationship. She did the checking up on me. She suggested we go out more. I didn't have the time for that shit. Besides, she was still holding out on me. We had been together for almost a whole year and hadn't had sex. Every time I tried to make my move, she resisted. I wasn't feeling that at all. I sent her ass to voicemail and went about my business.

KP's brown Maxima became a familiar car coming in and out of the apartment. This became a routine for him. A little kid no more than twelve would hop out of the car and head into the building. He wouldn't come out until KP came back to pick him up later that night. I put two and two together, and knowing KP, he had the youngster working for him. Every day for the last couple of weeks, this was the norm.

I became a creature of habit. Trying to avoid being

detected by KP or anyone associated with him. Not out of fear, but instincts. My intuition didn't agree well with this nigga around, so I did everything in my power to dodge him. Pouchon hadn't been back around since I saw him with KP. Uno had been blowing my phone up for the last couple of days, but I ignored his calls. He left messages for me to call him back. At times, I wanted to return the calls, but living this lifestyle... shit, your mind can go from one thing to the next in a drop of a dime.

Rah had been getting really sloppy lately. The count was fucked up on the work, and the amount we were moving declined. I was too busy trying to get something else set up and didn't take charge.

I came into the building one night after spending a few hours with Avia and her family. I had promised to come around more often since I had been busy, so I was trying to hold on to my end of the bargain.

Rah was in the middle of the open hallway a few doors away from his mom's apartment, making a sale. He was doing the same thing he vowed not to do. When he saw me, he had this pathetic, nonchalant attitude, then I told him he was slipping, he shrugged it off like it was nothing. Because of that one slip, it caused a whole bunch of shit to hit the fan.

"How many sodas did you say we had left, Rah?" I asked from the kitchen counter.

I was counting money because tomorrow was a re-up day. Russ put a deal on the table so I couldn't refuse. He confessed to me that he was going to show love on a whole brick of cocaine. He even mentioned KP's name, saying he was going to tax them new niggas, but for me, he'll do me a solid for eighteen thousand. I did everything in my power to get eighteen thousand up for a brick. Even if it meant cutting out all my habits, like shopping for shoes and smoking.

"I don't know, let me check when this shit goes on commercial, fool," Rah said.

He sat with a joint halfway out of his mouth. This dude was getting on my nerves.

"Come on, fool, I asked you to count that shit before I left, bro, you on some other shit." I sighed, turning to face him.

"What do you mean, fool? I'm watching something. I told you imma, check that shit. I don't know why you tripping for," he said agitated, letting out a cough. His smoke-filled lungs couldn't take in and let out air while trying to speak.

"Miss me with all that, nigga. Count the shit so I could get this bread up for the next batch. I need to go," I said. I was tired of babysitting this lazy-ass nigga, and it was getting on my nerves.

"Nigga, who are you telling what to do, nigga? You don't run shit. Matter of fact, why won't count that shit yourself?" he yelled.

In the same instance, I put the money down and was in his chest. He stood up challenging me, but his eyes didn't hold my stare. Rah had a height advantage by an inch or two. Toe to toe, I didn't care who won, I just wanted to show him this was a win or loss for me.

"Fuck-nigga, you think everything is a game. Nigga, you slipping heavy, and you don't even see it. The money ain't right, Rah, and I got a deal on the table for us," I said, pointing at his chest. "I asked your punk-ass already, nigga. Now count that shit nigga before we make a mess of your mama's shit."

"Get out of my face, nigga," he said, sitting down without a word more.

His face was twisted, but I could tell he weighed out his options. I walked back over to the kitchen and tried to focus on counting the rest of the money. The house was unusually quiet. The silence was fucking with my head. We only had fifteen thousand towards our goal, and if we tightened up, we had a whole day and night to get the other three grands up.

I was starting to feel like I couldn't really trust this nigga. Not like he would steal anything, but he was becoming a liability, and I had goals. It was almost time for his mom to come home, and this nigga still had a pistol on the living room table, a couple of baggies, and crack lying naked on the kitchen counter. I had to Saran Wrap the money to take to Ma June's apartment and put it in our stash. After this one brick, I thought about splitting whatever we made evenly and going my way. Right now, I was holding the weight, and it was becoming a burden.

KNOCK. KNOCK. KNOCK.

"Who is that?" I asked instinctively.

"Damn, fool, that might be my old girl," Rah said.

"Hell Nah, nigga, she got keys stupid. Why the fuck would she be knocking?" I asked.

BANG.BANG. BANG

"This is the Miami Metro Police Department. Open up!"

I ran to Rah's room, quickly throwing the money I had deep down in dirty clothes. I didn't know what to do next. Rah was still in the living room stuck on stupid, probably still feeling the effect of his high.

"Nigga, come on, we got to get the fuck out this crib, nigga!" I yelled, sweeping all the drugs into the garbage can in the kitchen.

Some of it I had to dust into the kitchen sink, running hot water over it.

'BANG.BANG. BANG'

"Ok, on the count of five, we are coming in!" the police yelled.

"Fuck this shit!" I said, running to the bathroom window where I was trying to climb out, only to find an M-16 pointed at my face.

"Don't you fucking move!"

My inner thought spoke before the police did. I've seen this scene play out too many times.

"Don't you move, motherfucker!" a guy in a ski mask yelled. My body froze automatically. Everything that happened next was against my will. I wasn't about to move a limb.

"Get on the floor. Get down on the floor," another voice boomed, pulling me out the window by my shirt collar. They had the place surrounded. I heard the helicopter above me circle in the night air.

Lights flashed, and sirens roared in the silent air. I put my head on the damp grass in shame as the officers jumped on my back, pulling up my arms in the air as if they were trying to break them. Though I was in pain, I stayed very still as the sound of handcuffs, cold to the touch, tightened around my wrists. I was a habitual juvenile offender, and there were guns, drug money, and drugs in Rah's mother's apartment. I asked Rah to put all the shit at Ma June's house before I asked him to count. How did this shit go left?

"Damn!" was all I could say. "Damn, damn, damn!"

CHAPTER TWENTY-EIGHT

I hit juvenile hall, running. I knew I was in it for the long haul after what happened at the apartment. All of us were in for the ride. What I didn't know was how serious this situation was. The reason Rah G was acting weird unbeknownst to me was that KP got him involved in some serious shit. He had dealings with this nigga KP behind my back all along.

I sat in the holding tank, awaiting booking for the charges they had Rah and me on. The room was simply furnished; four white walls, a brown table, metal chairs, and a fucking A.C. vent that was driving me crazy. The hole in my shirt didn't make it any better. The air came out like a blower, high, and super cold. I thought I was going to get frostbite. My whole body was numb.

When the leading detective came through the door, I warmed up quickly. His long face was decorated with bad acne. He had a nose like a boxer who had lost too many fights. If I didn't know better, I would swear he never smiled a day in his life.

"Mahkahi Guierra, I'm Detective Saunders," he said, sitting in an empty seat opposite me. "I'm sure you know why you've been arrested?" he questioned.

"Nah, not really. Ain't nobody telling me nothing," I said honestly. "If I had to tell it, I didn't get caught with shit. I was out the window, face down when they got me."

He shook his head like he agreed with me. He studied me for a while.

"So, you're just here for nothing, huh? You haven't done anything like they all say," he said. He became more serious but controlled. I had never seen this guy until someone mentioned his name during my arrest. He was getting at me like I did something to him personally. "Tell me what I did then, jump out the window? What kind of charge is that?" I questioned.

"Are you getting smart with me, boy?" he challenged, losing his temper. He got up and stood right behind me, coming within inches of my ear.

"I'm going to tell you what. Your homeboy, what's his name? Rah G, implicated you in a murder involving your drug supplier Russell Brooks, a.k.a., Russ. Apparently, Rah G and your man Kaship Price, a.k.a., KP robbed Russy for some dope and named you as the get-away driver," he said.

My mouth hung open, not believing what this man was telling me. The hair on the back of my neck and arms stood straight up.

"What?" I managed to say.

"What? You still don't know what I'm talking about? I can't help you in court if you don't tell me the truth," the detective said, walking back to his seat.

"Man, you fucking with me," I said. I had so many questions.

First off, I was wondering what the fuck he was talking about? Murder? Did Rah put my name in some shit for real? Why did he hit up Russ, and not tell me? That nigga KP, it had to be him. Then the words most cops hated to hear escaped my mouth.

"I'm a minor, get me a lawyer," I said. This had to be some bullshit. Had to be!

"OK, tough guy," he said, getting up from where he sat. "Shoot yourself. Accessory to murder carries up to...." He gave it some thought. "Let's just say you're young, an easy target for somebody's bitch in the penitentiary. By the time you get out, your name will be Ms. Guierra," he said, letting out a disturbing laugh. He got up and left, leaving me confused.

For the next few months, I sat in juvenile hall, the same place the judge told me he didn't want to see me again. I managed to bring my ass right back to this shit. This time, I was in the permanent unit, module seven. The Haitians and Yanks (black Americans) couldn't stand each other. I went through this same segregated shit at Jann Mann. It was ten times worse in juvenile hall. The fights were hour after hour. No lockdowns. Just straight gladiator school. Sometimes the guards would place bets against a Haitian or Yank fight.

It was chaotic. Haitians nicknamed "Zoe" in creole had a reputation that dated back to my life in Little Haiti. Because they migrated from the island at a young age, they weren't used to the American ways. Thus, the bullying started, until one day, Haitians fought back and claimed the name Zoe, which meant bones. It's said that when a Haitian hit you, it felt like bones smashing against your face.

The details of what I was charged with came to me a couple of days before, just as the detective said. This stupid-ass nigga Rah G got himself in a jam fucking with KP. They took Rah to the country jail, where he was tried as an adult. KP was charged with the murder, and Rah G was charged as an accessory. My lawyer said Rah never told the detective anything. The detective was playing with my head. I was charged with the dope found in the house. The police took everything, including money. The lawyer got them to drop the charges since I didn't have shit. But because of my background, and the probation violation, I was going to a program.

They were gunning for me real bad. They talked about putting me in a level Eight or Level Ten Program. Damn, I hadn't even been to a level six or an out-custody program. I never so much as talked to anyone about the shit I have been through. How could they try and send me straight to juvenile prison? I couldn't remember the last time I saw my probation officer. I knew this was some bullshit. I went back to square one.

• • •

My lawyer decided to write a letter to the committee so that I could read it to them during sentencing. He said if I wrote the letter, I would have to base it on my life and apologize for my actions. My lawyer figured, maybe I could soften their heart to do what's fair.

I went to my three-man cell. It wasn't much different from the process units. The cell was more of a housing unit and better than being stuck in the main building twenty-four-seven. I shared the room with two other kids who were from Lil Haiti: Ticaca and Smoke. We were all from the hood, even though I moved away a long time ago. Though they were from a different section of Lil Haiti, they were the home team. I would hate to have to share the room with one of those off-brand niggas that was there. When I laid on my mat, I got lost thinking about Avia. What could she be doing right now? Was she even thinking about me? Then I remembered what needed to be done, so I started to write.

To whom it may concern…
My name is Mahkahi Guierra. My lawyer told me to write this letter to apologize for my actions. I'm sorry

for being whom I am. It's hard enough people won't understand something they never experienced for themselves. It's hard enough to be judged by people that only know your life story from a piece of paper they've read or by what someone else perceived to be the truth. No one ever asked me for my side of things or what kind of help I needed. It's always just been about what others recommended. Honestly, I don't even want anyone to feel sorry for me. I know the outcome of this meeting will be judged solely by what everyone else feels. I just need to once that you put yourself in my shoes or better yet what you would do if your family Member or children were put in this position?

Thank you.

Satisfied, I folded the piece of paper and stuck it in my shoe. I planned on memorizing it line for line. Instead of being naïve to what I already knew the state was going to do, I just kept it one hundred. I had one more thing to do, which was talking to Avia about where we stood. The life I was living had too much room for error, and even though I had strong feelings for her, I had to let her go.

I walked through the dayroom looking for Ticaca, who I knew was probably on the other side of the octagon-shaped unit playing dominos. Just in case he wasn't, I looked in a small TV room that played movies on the weekends, but he wasn't there. I needed someone to watch my back while I used the phone. The likelihood of being jumped by a Yank was at an all-time high. We were already outnumbered. There was peace because we had heart. Besides that, I wasn't worried about LZ coming back for a probation violation. It made me feel at ease. I had my brother from another mother around to clean up anything that went down. With both of us together, shit was definitely looking ugly for the opposing team.

"Ticaca, I'm about to get on this pipe right quick," I told him, referring to the phone. He and Smoke had a serious game of Capi Coo going on, and they seemed to be down a few points.

"You are supposed to play the two. You see me turning sixes so you can pass him and let me play. Fool, you're garbage, man!" Twin yelled at Smoke.

Smoke sat silently, realizing that he had fucked up. Ticaca liked to talk shit, and he had the hands to back it up. He was an identical twin to the notorious Scarface. Together they terrorized the streets of Lil Haiti. When you mentioned the twins, you were talking about Ticaca and Scarface. Smoke, on the other hand, was a passive-aggressive type of kid. He waited until the action started, and when it did, he reminded me of LZ's brother Trigga. He ain't give a fuck if you were big or a midget, if you moved like you wanted some smoke, he was ready to light the fire.

"Yo, Ticaca, you heard me, fool?" I asked, putting my back to the phone. "I said I'm about to get on the pipe right quick," I repeated again, just for assurance.

"Alright, alright. Hey, amigo? Yeah, you. You want to play with this nigga here, basura?" he said, pointing to Smoke. Smoke got up unaffected. He knew how Ticaca was, but he loved the young nigga's energy. He walked over to where Ticaca stood, watching them play, then nodded his head towards me. I looked around before dialing Avia's number.

Avia's mother picked up and yelled for Avia to get the phone. I explained to her the hardship I was about to endure and told her how much I cared about her. She wondered why it took so long for me to call. Every time she tried to pry into my thoughts, I had no explanation except that I just couldn't fuck with her like that anymore. We spoke briefly as I told her our relationship was over. She protested for a while, trying to give the reason why she would hold out for me and so forth, but I managed to convince her that it was for the best. It was bad enough. I barely had any moral support. But fuck it. We said our goodbyes and that was it.

When I got back to my room, I couldn't wait for the day of sentencing. I was going to speak my mind. If it's a letter the lawyer wanted me to give, then so be it. I was going to give them a piece of my mind too.

CHAPTER TWENTY-NINE

I memorized my letter from top to bottom, over and over. I recited the words until they became the second language to me. Twin and I sat on the bench awaiting our fate while his mother, his identical twin brother, and my lawyer all sat on the other side of the fence that separated us.

"Ain't no telling what these crackers tryna do, kid," Twin said, looking in his mother's direction. We had a clear view of the other side where people waited to get into the building. Between both of us, only one bench sat outside on each side of the fence.

Our families came through an unauthorized gate escorted by a guard to sit on the lone bench. We came through a long corridor connected to the dorms to sit and wait. I didn't have any faith in anybody other than my lawyer to come and represent for me. Personally, the way I was feeling, I ain't give a fuck. I was lost and adjusted to this life I was living.

"Don't matter to me," I said, staring in the same direction Twin was staring. "They are gonna do what the fuck they want at the end of the day. Whatever they do, they could run it, like whatever," I said.

Twin's brother looked around the small space in disgust, the frown on his face evidence he wasn't comfortable being there. As I sat staring at his mother, I noticed the deep conversation she was having with my lawyer. Her mannerism reminded me of my mother's when she was speaking to someone about important business. She had the tendency to put her hands together on her lap, with each finger inter-locked. Attentive. Watching the person speak, as if every-thing they said held value.

My lawyer was probably running game as usual. Sud-denly, I was sad. I almost let the cloud of water in my eyes escape thinking about my mother.

"You are right, my nigga! They are gonna do what they are gonna do anyways," Twin said, shrugging his shoul-ders. He sat straight back, the cuffs around his wrists rat-tling as he moved. I hung my head low, waiting to see who they would call first. Since my name came before the twins, I knew I was next.

"Monnier, come on," the fat guard yelled from the open door. I looked up to see if he was mistaken, but he was call-ing Twin before me.

"Who me?" Twin asked.

"Yeah, ain't your name M.O.N.N.I.E.R.?" The guard asked, spelling out his name while he ran his beefy fingers along with the little card he had in his hand.

Twin got up reluctantly, looking towards his mother across the fence.

Before he could make it all the way inside, the door to the same building opened on the other side, and another guard led his mother and brother into the building. I sat there thoughtless, watching the clouds from under the pavilion. It got dark fast, as thunder peeked from behind the clouds.

The quiet afternoon was cool, as lightning lit up the semi-dark skies, followed by a loud roar. The cool air moved quickly, picking up leaves and spinning them around from time to time. As little drops of water made their way towards me from the corner of the rooftop. I heard, "Guierra, come on. Damn, it's raining," the guard said, looking towards the sky."

244 | THE STREET ANALYST

No shit, Sherlock

On my way in, Twin was on his way out, head held high with a smile plastered on his face. We held eye contact, and he silently mouthed the word 'six' to me. I thought to myself, he has a record as long as mine. There was no way in hell they were going to give me anything more than a Level Six program. But with my luck, who knew.

I took in the scene, a room full of familiar white faces, with only two blacks: I and a woman dressed in a red suit. When I walked into the room, no one acknowledged me, but the smile on the woman's face sent chills down my spine.

The long table reminded me of the last supper when Jesus sat in the middle, passing out the bread. The judge sat in the middle of the table in Jesus's place, with a stack of brown folders. Four people sat on either side to my right and left.

"Mr. Guierra, sit down," the judge commanded.

I did as I was told. The door flew open as my lawyer ushered in with a small umbrella. The rain beat him inside as he tried to close the door with one hand.

"Sorry, I had to take an important call," he said, leaning the umbrella against the wall.

All the people in the room gave him an unsympathetic look. After my lawyer squeezed his way in between the rest of the clan, I noticed how quickly they forgave him.

They all greeted him by his first name. These mother-fuckers smiled at each other like they knew something I didn't.

It gave me the notion that I was about to get fucked over. I don't know why I started to feel as if the sun was sitting on my neck. My palms were sweaty, and my air supply felt short. Something was making me sick to my stomach.

• • •

They all went back and forth for five minutes, trying to decide which program best fits my record. My lawyer didn't put up a good fight. For what he was worth, he might as well let me defend myself. My past and present came up more than once, and all he did was agree to disagree.

Then he capped it off with a smile, saying, "My client would like to say something to the board." He looked at me, giving his approval for me to speak. I was tight-lipped, mad as hell how this motherfucker was trying to play me. Since last night, I had been reciting this letter. Suddenly, when it came to time for me to speak, I wanted to punch this cracker in his shit.

The first few words came out, "Um. Um. Um. Hold up," I said, looking at all their pale faces. The lady in the red suit, though she wasn't looking dead at me, had the same smirk on her face. My mind seemed like it started playing tricks on me.

I closed my eyes, and out of somewhere deep down, I lunged up and grabbed my lawyer, and punched his face until I saw red. The people in the room jumped out of the way. The guards were trying to pry me off him, while my chest heaved up and down. My fist drove into his blood-stricken face. It felt good for the moment. I wanted to claw his eyes out, but I thought about the trouble I was already in. Surely, I was going to juvenile prison for this shit. If you asked me, I wouldn't have done anything differently. To hell with him.

"Mr. Guierra, can you go forward with your letter, sir?"

The voice caused me to open my eyes. Everyone was looking straight at me. I felt like a freak for the movie that just played in my head. I must have zoned out again. As I began to recite what I wrote, word for word. They were so articulate, like poetry, as I read them from the top of my head. I saw each letter dance before my eyes to formulate what I was feeling. You should have seen the looks on their faces, exactly what I expected, pure shock.

When I was done, the judge and my lawyer sat back, arms over their chest, clearing their throats in unison. The judge shook his head, looking down at something on the table. Everybody followed suit until he cleared his throat then again for a second time, getting everybody's attention.

A paper went around the table to everyone but the black lady in the red suit and me. It went all the way around silently until it got back to the judge. They looked at each other shaking their heads in unison.

"Mr. Guierra is that all you have to say?" the judge asked, looking at me intently. I wanted to say, 'fuck you, cracker!' But instead, I said, "Yeah."

As I walked out of there that day, I didn't have that chip on my shoulder. Just like Twin, I walked out of there with my head held high, with a smile on my face as wide as the Everglades. I looked back to the corridor. The lady in the red suit finally spoke.

"You shot out!" she mouthed. Nobody but me seemed to notice.

She finally said something.

The cool air hit my face when I was out the door. I looked up, and the light blue skies were now clear.

"I know," I mouthed to myself, laughing slightly.

"You OK?" the guard asked, shaking my arm.

"Never felt better, fool," I responded with excitement walking towards the dorms. Well, I guess I already knew the verdict—Level Eight. My nine to twelve sentences were just another bump in the road. I'll be back. I always come back, but this time imma goes harder than before. Just watch.

EPILOGUE

July 4ᵗʰ...

L Z, Ace, Lil V, Pouchon, Monte, and a couple of other people were out in front of 2150 having a ball. Drinking, smoking, and God only knows what else. Big D stood in front of the 2020 buildings between a row of cars smoking a cigarette, watching the block while the people he was with, hideout in the building. Police had been riding by, and shit was getting hot.

'POP, POP, POP.... PLRAAP, PAP, PAP'

The sound of firecrackers could be heard in the distance. Not far from where Big D stood, some kids were setting up to make the night sky light up with their fireworks.

A dark-colored car crept slowly up the block and caught his attention. As it rode by, Big D contemplated if he should run, knowing if it were the police, they were going to harass him. His better judgment made him play it out. Staring into the dark grey car, the only thing he could see were four shadows; two people in the back seat, and the two people in the front, dressed in all black. As it passed, the driver of the car seemed to lean back in his seat, making Big D uncomfortable. When the car disappeared around the block, Big D called out to the others in the building, signaling that it might be the police.

"Tiki, check this out, fool," Big D yelled out.

Tiki was in the building, scheming on a young nigga who claimed he was the best dice player around. For Tiki, right now was not a good time to be interrupted. Especially when he was down a few dollars. Tiki came running out of the building, sweat forming on his forehead from the excitement of the game.

"What's up, kid? You know a nigga in there shooting. I'm damned fooled, this young nigga got the bank, I can't let them get off like that," he said, wiping his sweat bead off his forehead.

Something down the street got Tiki's attention. When Big D looked in the same direction, he felt a rush of anxiety that didn't sit well with him.

"That's the shit I was gonna tell you about. That car came through here already. That shit looks like it's up to something. I can't tell if it's the police or the Jack Boys," Big D said.

They both watched the car as it turned down another block before coming in front of 2020.

"Let's dip my nigga, this shit is getting creepy," Big D said, still looking in the direction of where the car turned.

"Who is that down the block acting like a fool?' Tiki asked, stepping out in the street.

Ace and they were so caught up in themselves they didn't seem to notice. Unbeknownst to Tiki, someone did notice, just didn't pay it more attention.

"Let me call Lil V and see if he is down there. I gotta let him know that whip is circulating heavy," Tiki said, picking up the phone, dialing his number.

"Are you coming back because we are about to keep the game crunk? My hands are getting cold, bro," the youngster said, poking his head out of the building.

"Go ahead, jit, you got that," Tiki said, waving him off. In all actuality, he was mad he couldn't win his money back, but that day would be a day he would never regret.

"Hey V, watch out for the whips that keep circulating," Tiki said, speaking into the receiver.

Lil V didn't ask where it was at. He simply said 'OK' and hung up.

"Hey Big D, let's clear it, fool." Tiki and Big D jumped in Tiki's car and left Victory Park.

20 minutes later...

Pouchon stood across the street from 2150, where a strange car with dark tinted windows rode by several times. He watched the car creep slowly up the block, riding in front of 2020 slowly. He could tell from where he stood that someone was in front of 2020. Oblivious to the phone call Lil V just received, Pouchon brushed it off as just another car passing through. And if it was the police, nobody at 2150 was out doing anything. It was the fourth of July, and they were there to just have fun. Pouchon scurried off across the street from 2020 quickly, in need of another drink.

"Come on, you'll," he yelled. When everybody looked in his direction, he held up a bottle. Everybody ran to get a refill.

The car pulled up, watching the click of people with their backs turned, impatiently waiting for their drinks. The car parked backward in front of 2150. When Pouchon saw the car, he swallowed his heart when all four doors flew open simultaneously.

"Oh, shit!" was all he managed to get out of his mouth as four masked men jumped out, guns blazing.

"UGH!" yelled Monte as he was shot a point-blank range in his torso. Before he could move, the first gunman was on him.

Pouchon froze, the bottle still in his hand as he watched Monte scream in agony from his pain. Before Monte got a chance to take a breath, another shot tore through his arm. The bullet flipped him on his way to the ground.

The bottle of Cognac Pouchon held in his hand, exploded, waking him from his trance. At that moment, he took off running. Everything happened so fast, it seemed as if everybody had a delayed reaction. Laying on the ground, Monte could feel his life slipping away.

"As I walk through the…," Monte' recited.

'PA, PA, PA'

The gunmen interrupted his thoughts, standing over him and emptying his clip into Monte's body. Monte shook violently as the bullets danced around in his flesh.

The other three gunmen ran after the rest of the crew, hitting Ace in the ankle and finger. Ace took one good look at his finger hanging by a limb and ran harder, avoiding another bullet as it whizzed past his head.

LZ wasn't as lucky. The gunman chased his prey down an alley behind the buildings across the street from 2150.

'POP, POP, POP'

The gunmen let off three rapid shots, only hitting LZ once, slowing him down. The bullet ripped off through his back, sending him flying forward. The shot caused LZ to lose his balance. As the gunmen got closer, he let off a couple more shots, hitting LZ in the back of the leg, dropping him instantly.

"Ahhhh, man, fuck!" LZ screamed.

The gunman, out of breath, caught up to his target, smiling behind his mask. He looked around the alley, satisfied they were alone. He stood over LZ, letting off eight more shots from LZ's chest on down.

Lil V was in the cut, watching him cowardly behind some bushes. The gunman pulled the trigger one more time for good measure, but the gun jammed up. He slapped the pistol in his palm, all the while LZ squirmed on the ground in pain, looking up at his predator.

"Fuck you, puss-ass nigga!" LZ managed to say before spitting blood to his side.

He was still trying to move despite getting hit so many times. Realizing the gun wasn't going to work, he stepped over LZ and looked around.

The dark skies lit up in different colors as fireworks boomed in the air. The people around oblivious to the mayhem in Victory Park. Just another loud Fourth of July.

The gunman slapped the side of his head, but he couldn't finish the job. With that, he ran off in the direction where they parked and hopped in the waiting car as it sped off.

Lil V poked his head out of the bushes making sure the coast was clear. He hesitantly walked over to his friend, scanning the alleyway.

"Damn!" he whispered, burying his face in his hand.

Lil V hurried over to LZ, cradling his neck. LZ was trying to say something, flinging his arms around like an octopus. LZ finally managed to spit the blood from his mouth.

"Call my mom, fool!" LZ begged.

Then his eyes fluttered as his body twitched in Lil V's arms. Several cars pulled into the alley, scaring the shit out of Lil V. He was about to drop LZ and run.

"Freeze!" Someone yelled.

He put LZ head down gently. Looking in the direction of the light, he put his hands up.

The memory slowly began to hunt Lil V from the warning Tiki gave him earlier.

'Hey V, it's a whip that keeps circulating. You'll need to watch that shit.'

Lil V shook his head disgracefully, disappointed in

himself. He thought of a story he would concoct to save face with his friends.

"Help! Please help me! He's dying!" Lil V yelled, looking at his friends in the alley while his hands remained in the air.

Would this be the end?

ABOUT THE AUTHOR

Peterson "YcDaChamp" Jean

As a music artist and serial entrepreneur, Peterson "YcDa-Champ" Jean now adds "author" to his many hustles. Growing up in Miami, Florida, obstacles became his greatest fuel after being sentenced to 15 years and 8 months in federal prison for the manufacture and distribution of crack cocaine. While in prison, he ventured into the world of books and found himself, ultimately rebuilding his life after his release.

As a true entrepreneur, Peterson established and created Panacea Artist Development Group LLC and One-way Victory Publication, creating an empire that is destined to thrive in the business world. His road to success is unwavering as he brings you his first book, The Street Analyst, with more to follow. Peterson hasn't let his past define who he really is: intelligent, determined, self-motivated, and very much a hustler. When asked what inspires him, he simply answers, "Hunger!"

Made in the USA
Columbia, SC
22 December 2020

29648195R00143